Royal Navy
DESTROYERS
Since 1945

Royal Navy
DESTROYERS
Since 1945

Leo Marriott

LONDON

IAN ALLAN LTD

Contents

First published 1989

ISBN 0 7110 1817 0

Published by Ian Allan Ltd, Shepperton, Surrey; and printed by Ian Allan Printing Ltd at their works at Coombelands in Runnymede, England

Acknowledgements

As usual, the preparation of this book has only been possible with the help of many individuals and organisations who have devoted time and effort in providing me with information and material. I would particularly like to thank the following: Paul Kemp, Dept of Photographs, Imperial War Museum; G. J. A. Raven, Director of Naval History, Netherlands Ministry of Defence; S-Lt L. M. Holliday RN, HMS *Southampton*, S-Lt A. J. Dorricott RN, HMS *Liverpool*; Charles Hamilton and the staff at Skyfotos; Lt-Cdr W. R. J. Hockin RN, HMS *York*; Lt M. C. Stuttard RN, HMS *Cardiff*; Adrian Vicary, Maritime Photo Library; Lt-Cdr P. C. Maxwell RN, HMS *Cardiff*; Lt K. I. Thomas RN, HMS *Bristol*; Cdr R. S. Ainsley RN, HMS *Exeter*; Lt D. F. Randal RN, HMS *Edinburgh*; Lt R. M. Dolan RN, HMS *Manchester*; Lt S. E. J. David RN, HMS *Newcastle*; Photographic Section HMS *Osprey*; Mr R. W. Easton, Yarrow Shipbuilders; Mr A. Farrow, Ian Allan Ltd, for allowing me access to the Real Photos Collection and other material.

Front cover:
A fine picture of HMS *Manchester*, a Type 42 destroyer. *Royal Navy*

Glossary and Abbreviations

AA	Anti-Aircraft
ac	alternating current
ADAWS	Action Data Automated Weapons System
Arr	Arrived
AS	Anti-Submarine
ASW	Anti-Submarine Warfare
ASWE	Admiralty Surface Weapons Establishment
AW	Air Warning (radar)
B/Up	Broken Up
cal	calibre
CIWS	Close In Weapon System
COGOG	Combined Gas Turbine or Gas Turbine
COSAG	Combined Steam and Gas Turbine
CP	Central Pivot
CRBFD	Close Range Blind Fire Director
DC	Depth Charge
dc	direct current
DCT	Director Control Tower
D/F	Direction Finding
DP	Dual Purpose
DS	Destroyer Squadron
ESM	Electronic Surveillance Measures
F	Fahrenheit
FPB	Fast Patrol Boat
GW	General Warning (radar)
GWS	Guided Weapon System
HA	High Angle
HAS	Helicopter Anti-Submarine
HF/DF	High Frequency Direction Finding
HMAS	His/Her Majesty's Australian Ship
HMCS	His/Her Majesty's Canadian Ship
HMS	His/Her Majesty's Ship
IJN	Imperial Japanese Navy
IN	Indian Navy
IR.N	Iranian Navy
ISR.N	Israeli Navy
kt	knots
LA	Low Angle
Limbo	Three-barrelled anti-submarine mortar. Max range 2,000yd
MRS	Medium Range System
MTB	Motor Torpedo Boat
NGS	Naval Gunfire Support
nm	nautical miles
oa	overall
PN	Pakistan Navy
QF	Quick Firing
RAN	Royal Australian Navy
RBOC	Rapid Blooming Offboard Chaff
RCN	Royal Canadian Navy
RHN	Royal Hellenic Navy (Greece)
RN	Royal Navy
RNethN	Royal Netherlands Navy
RNN	Royal Norwegian Navy
RPC	Remote Power Control
SAN	South African Navy
shp	shaft horsepower
Squid	Three-barrelled anti-submarine mortar. Max range 300yd
STAAG	Stabilised Tachymetric Anti-Aircraft Gun
STD	Simple Tachymetric Director
STWS	Ships Torpedo Weapon System
TT	Torpedo Tubes
UHF	Ultra High Frequency
USN	United States Navy
VDS	Variable Depth Sonar
VHF	Very High Frequency

Introduction

Destroyer! The very word conjures up the traditional image of naval warfare with lean ships, bristling with guns and torpedoes, steaming at speed to attack an enemy battle fleet. Unfortunately, romantic images such as this bear little relationship to the reality of any form of warfare, particularly naval engagements in the 20th century. True, in World War 1 each side deployed major surface fleets screened by numerous flotillas of destroyers and there were many fast and furious actions. However, between 1939 and 1945 the nature of naval warfare underwent a fundamental change, mainly due to the massive increase in the effectiveness of airpower (both land and sea based) and consequently the duties and attributes required of the destroyer also changed. In the post-1945 era the situation has been made even more complex by the development of new weapons including guided missiles, the staggering evolution of radars and other electronic systems, the increased performance and lethality of modern aircraft, and of course the advent of the nuclear powered submarine.

In this modern world the role of surface warships has undergone several fundamental reappraisals and, indeed, some authorities even question whether there is any role for them at all in the face of air and undersea weapon systems. In any event the old wartime distinctions between various warship types has been blurred and lost, especially as far as the destroyer is concerned.

The traditional role of the destroyer was to protect the battlefleet from attacks by enemy destroyers, to launch torpedo attacks against the enemy battle line, and later to defend battlefleets and task forces against air and submarine attack. In addition they would be pressed into service in a variety of tasks including gunfire support of amphibious landings, convoy escort, blockade and neutrality patrols, special operations and, all too often, evacuation of defeated armies. Altogether they thoroughly earned the appellation 'maids of all work' in two world wars.

Since 1945 most of the traditional roles have changed or disappeared. The performance of modern submarines has meant that ASW is now a very specialised task requiring complex and expensive frigates, some of which carry substantial anti-ship and anti-aircraft weapon systems as well. Such vessels are far larger than any wartime destroyer and are infinitely more capable. At the

Below:
Armed with a variety of weapons including guided missiles, and bristling with electronic gear, HMS *Gloucester* is one of the Royal Navy's latest destroyers. *Vosper Thornycroft*

other end of the scale, although the battleship has virtually disappeared (apart from the rejuvenated 'Iowa' class ships of the USN), the mounting of significant anti-surface and long-range anti-aircraft missile batteries has led to larger cruiser-type ships displacing well over 10,000 tons.

These two trends have squeezed out the traditional destroyer and have led to a breed of ships which specialise in the anti-aircraft and anti-ship role but do not carry the full sophisticated ASW weapon fit of the modern frigate. Size is no indication of function. The Royal Navy's latest Type 22 frigates displace over 5,000 tons compared with some 4,500 tons for a stretched Type 42 destroyer. In the US Navy the current 'Spruance'

class destroyers are similar in size to the older 'Belknap' guided missile cruisers.

These changes are reflected in this book which will trace the history, progress and development of the destroyer in the Royal Navy following the end of World War 2. A previous book in this series covered the history of frigates in the same period and showed that, although numbers have decreased, there has been constant evolution and a continuous construction programme. Another volume covered aircraft carriers and, despite the decline and near-extinction of the carrier force in the 1970s, the situation today is much better with three modern ships in service backed up by various support vessels. Sadly, this book will relate a

eft:
size is no longer an indication of function with modern warships. The Navy's current Type 22 frigates, exemplified by HMS *Beaver*, are larger than Type 42 destroyer. *Royal Navy*

Below left:
Crowded destroyer pens on the Firth of Forth during World War 1. HMS *Patrician*, in the foreground, displaced 1,000 tons and was armed with three 4in guns and four torpedo tubes. *Author's Collection*

Below:
HMS *Wishart* was one of the 'Modified V and W' class launched in 1919 which represented the peak of destroyer development in World War 1. This photograph shows her appearance in May 1937. *Maritime Photo Library*

Bottom:
Apart from an increase in size, HMS *Amazon* closely followed the lines of the later 'V' and 'W' classes. Launched in 1926, she was one of two prototype designs which led to the standard prewar flotilla destroyer. *Real Photos (S1126)*

different tale. Since 1945 the numbers of destroyers in the Royal Navy has fallen relentlessly to the present total of only 13 ships. Worse still, there are none currently under construction and little evidence exists of any firm plans to build more. Given the current operational life of warships, it is quite possible that the Royal Navy will enter the 21st century with no destroyers in service.

The history of the destroyer in the Royal Navy dates back to the last decades of the 19th century and basically stems from the perfection of a practical torpedo in the 1870s. It was not long before most navies realised that small, fast torpedo-launching ships could threaten even the most powerful battlefleets by using their speed and manoeuvrability to avoid fire from heavy guns, in order to get close enough to launch their weapons. To combat this threat, a new type of ship designated torpedo boat destroyer was evolved. Originally these were powered by reciprocating engines as in the 'Rattlesnake' class (525 tons) of 1886 but it was the advent of the Parsons steam turbine which really gave these ships their real

character. By 1899, HMS *Viper*, one of the first turbine-powered ships, displaced 344 tons and could make 34kt. Although further reciprocating-engined ships were built (eg the 'River' class — 550 tons, 25kt) it was the 'Tribal' class of 1907 which could be considered the first fully effective destroyer design. At around 1,000 tons displacement they were capable of ocean-going deployment and their 27,000shp turbines gave them a speed of 33kt. Armament generally comprised three 12pdr guns and two 18in torpedo tubes. By this time the distinction between torpedo boats and torpedo boat destroyers was lost as ships of this size were capable of both offensive and defensive actions. Consequently the term 'torpedo boat destroyer' was abbreviated to 'destroyer' which became the accepted name for vessels of this type. Most of the early destroyers had a low freeboard and when driven hard in heavy weather were more like submarines than surface ships! Conditions on board were dreadful, but nevertheless a great spirit and enthusiasm was engendered aboard these small ships which has carried through to the present day.

During World War 1, destroyers increased in size and capabilities until by 1918 a typical 'V and W' class ship (built in large numbers) displaced around 1,450 tons and was armed with four 4in guns and four 21in torpedo tubes in twin mountings. The final 'Modified V and Ws' were similar but with armament upgraded to four 4.7in guns and six 21in torpedo tubes. During the war the destroyers were grouped into flotillas of up to 20 ships, each led by a light cruiser or an enlarged destroyer known as a flotilla leader. Typical of the latter were the 'Shakespeare' class of 1,550 tons

which carried five 4.7in guns and six 21in torpedo tubes as well as extra accommodation for the flotilla staff officers.

The end of World War 1 naturally led to a halt in destroyer construction and development. No less than 44 orders were cancelled and many older and obsolete ships were scrapped. Construction of the remaining 'V and W' ships, together with the 'Shakespeare' class leaders, continued at a slow pace. It was not until 1925 that further orders for destroyers were placed and this was as a result of an invitation for tenders from all the major shipbuilders for a standard design. In the event two vessels were ordered, one each from Yarrow and Thornycroft, and named *Ambuscade* and *Amazon* respectively. Both ships were armed with

Below:
HMS *Brilliant*, launched in 1930, was typical of the prewar destroyers with an armament of four 4.7in guns, two single 2pdrs, a few machine guns for AA defence, and eight 21in torpedo tubes.
Author's Collection

Right:
The epitome of British destroyer design prior to the outbreak of war was the famous 'Tribal' class. HMS *Cossack* presents a stirring sight whilst on trials in 1938. She was lost in action during the war, along with most of her sister ships. *Real Photos (S1457)*

Below right:
The 'J' class represented an attempt to produce a smaller destroyer than the preceding 'Tribal' class and the resulting design formed the basis for much of the wartime construction programme. This photo shows HMS *Jervis* in 1939. *Maritime Photo Library*

our 4.7in and two 2pdr guns as well as six 21in torpedo tubes, and followed the basic outline of the 'V and Ws' with a raised forecastle and superfiring guns fore and aft. The Thornycroft ship was slightly larger with a length overall of 323ft and a standard displacement of 1,352 tons. Comparable figures for *Ambuscade*, the Yarrow ship, were 322ft and 1,173 tons. Both could make 37kt and had a range of around 3,300 miles at 15kt. Improved fire control arrangements were provided which consisted of a director and rangefinder mounted high up on the after part of the bridge and a fire control table in a transmitting station below decks.

Both ships were launched in 1926 and, with detail modifications, provided the basis for the standard Royal Navy fleet destroyer between the wars. It was that Service's policy to build destroyers in flotillas of eight ships together with a slightly enlarged flotilla leader. Thus eight 'A' class plus a leader (HMS *Codrington*) were completed in 1930 with further flotillas following at roughly yearly intervals, each bearing names in alphabetical progression. As an economy measure and at the height of prewar disarmament fever, the 1931 flotilla ('C' class) was cut to only four ships plus a leader and in fact these were all transferred to the Royal Canadian Navy just prior to World War 2. Otherwise construction continued at an increasing pace as the diplomatic situation deteriorated in the 1930s. The final prewar standard destroyers were the 'I' class launched in 1936-37 and although

2934

displacement and dimensions were almost identical to the *Amazon* of 1926, torpedo armament was now 10 21in tubes in two quintuple mountings, light AA armament was slightly increased and bunkerage increased to give a range of 5,500 miles at 15kt.

Although the Royal Navy thus built up a sizeable fleet of modern destroyers, by the mid 1930s they were faced with the fact that most foreign navies were building ships which were (on paper at least) larger, faster and better armed. In response to this a completely new design was drawn up with the emphasis on a heavy gun battery so that support could be given to the more lightly armed standard flotillas. The new ships were the famous 'Tribal' class and a total of 16 were laid down in 1936-37, all being completed by March 1939. Armament was eight 4.7in guns in four twin

turrets together with a four-barrelled 2pdr pom-pom and eight 0.5in AA machine guns, while only one quadruple torpedo mounting was carried. In addition to the British units, several others were built for the Australian and Canadian navies.

With war imminent, it was decided to revert to a slightly smaller design which would, hopefully, retain the best features of the 'Tribals' and be more powerful than the previous 'A' to 'I' classes. The result was the 16 ships of the 'J' and 'K' classes, together with a further eight of the 'N' class. At 1,760 tons standard displacement, they were only slightly smaller than the 'Tribals' and shipped six 4.7in guns and 10 21in torpedo tubes. However, a change from three to two boilers of greater capacity resulted in a hull which was 20ft shorter and necessitated only a single broad funnel — the first British destroyers with this feature.

Most of these ships were completed early in the war (with the exception of the 'N' class which were not launched until 1941).

As soon as hostilities commenced a number of major defects in British destroyer design quickly

Left:
HMS *Marne* was one of 16 'L' and 'M' class destroyers launched between 1940 and 1942. With their imposing gun turrets they were often thought to be the most handsome of the British wartime destroyers. *Author's Collection*

Below left:
From 1940 onwards destroyer construction centred on the standard emergency destroyer design typified by HMS *Ulster*. Based on the 'J' class hull and machinery, they were generally armed with four 4.7in guns, a variety of light AA guns including 2pdrs, 40mm and 20mm, and eight 21in torpedo tubes. *Real Photos (2934)*

Below:
The ultimate wartime destroyers were the 'Battle' class armed with four DP 4.7in guns in twin turrets forward and a heavy 40mm AA battery aft. A full torpedo outfit was carried and displacement had risen to over 3,000 tons at full load. Most of the class were completed too late to see any action. *Imperial War Museum*

became apparent. Although the Admiralty had been aware of the potential problems of air attack, they had failed to perfect a high-angle mounting for destroyer guns and consequently the maximum elevation of the standard 4.7in gun was only 40° — fine for surface actions but almost useless against aircraft. As far back as 1928 a 60° elevation mounting had been specified, but had proved to be unsatisfactory and nothing further had been done (although a high-angle 4.5in mounting was available for capital ships in the 1930s, none was made available for destroyers). Coupled to the lack of suitable mountings was the poor performance of the fire control systems in the AA mode, and finally the light AA armament of machine guns and a few 2pdrs proved totally inadequate.

The story of British destroyer development between 1939 and 1945 was primarily one of trying to overcome these deficiencies while at the same time operating in the face of generally overwhelming enemy air superiority. The result was a foregone conclusion and no less than 57 British destroyers were sunk by air attack including six of the 'Tribals' and seven of the 'J' and 'K' classes. Existing destroyers had their light AA armaments increased by the addition of extra 2pdrs, 20mm and 40mm guns as they became available and several landed one set of torpedo tubes in order to ship a 4in AA gun.

A slight improvement came about with the 'L' and 'M' classes which, utilising the basic 'J' class hull and machinery, were intended to carry six 4.7in guns in a new turret design which allowed 50° elevation. In fact, a shortage of the new mountings meant that four of the eight 'L' class were armed with eight 4in DP guns in four twin mountings — not such a bad substitution as it gave them the best destroyer AA firepower in the fleet; consequently they were very popular for escort duties in the Mediterranean where, sadly, they were all sunk in action.

The pressing needs of wartime construction, increased by the heavy losses experienced off Norway and Dunkirk, led to the abandonment of the large fleet destroyers requiring complex gun mountings which were in short supply. Instead, a new standard design was drawn up, which was slightly smaller than the 'J' class but retained the same machinery and featured a simple armament of four 4.7in guns and eight 21in torpedo tubes together with the best light AA armament available — generally a few 20mm and 2pdr guns. This became the 'O' class, which entered service in 1942 and was followed by the similar 'P' class which had five 4in guns to give a better AA armament. The succeeding 'Q' and 'R' classes reverted to the dimensions of the 'J' class hull but were otherwise similar to the eight 'O' class ships.

The 'S' class, which entered service in 1943, featured a new 4.7in mounting with 55° elevation and set the pattern for the remaining wartime standard destroyer construction ('T', 'U', 'V', 'W' and 'Z' classes). The 'Z' class introduced the 4.5in

gun as the new standard for British destroyers (as it is to this day), and the succeeding 32 'C' class ships, mostly completed after the war, were basically a perpetuation of the 'Z' class design. In all, 132 of the standard wartime destroyer design based on the 'O' class, right through to the 'C' groups, were built between 1940 and 1946.

The ships which finally put all the hard-gained war experience to use and provided the Royal Navy with a first class fleet destroyer were the 'Battle' class of the 1942 and 1943 construction programmes. At last a full dual-purpose, twin

Top:
The 'Daring' class, completed in the 1950s, were an expansion of the 'Battle' class design and were the last of the Royal Navy's conventional destroyers. *Imperial War Museum*

Top right:
Indian summer of the gun-armed destroyer. Three 'Battle' and one 'Weapon' class destroyers form the 7th Destroyer Squadron at Malta in the early 1960s. *Imperial War Museum*

Right:
The modern destroyer is a vehicle for the long range surface-to-air missile. HMS *Glamorgan* was one of eight 'County' class guided missile-armed destroyers built for the Royal Navy between 1959 and 1971. Their design was the result of a long and painful reappraisal of the role of the Royal Navy and its warships in the postwar era. *Royal Navy*

4.5in mounting was available giving 80° elevation. A heavy battery of 20mm and 40mm light AA guns was also carried in addition to a full complement of torpedoes (eight or 10 tubes depending on the sub-group). However, they were big ships, of 2,550 tons standard displacement, and delays with the fire control equipment meant that few were ready for service by the end of the war. A smaller design, the 'Weapon' class, intended to complement the 'Battles' was also put into production but none were completed during the war and most were cancelled in 1945.

In the postwar era, the only new conventional destroyer design to enter service was the 'Daring' class, basically developed from the 'Battles', whose construction proceeded at a snail's pace so that they did not enter service until the 1950s. After that, as this book will tell, confusion about the role of the destroyer, together with the advent of the guided missile, led first to the eight 'County' class guided missile destroyers and in turn to the one Type 82 and 12 Type 42 destroyers which are the last bearers of the destroyer tradition in the Royal Navy.

1 The Flotillas Disperse

World War 2 lasted for almost exactly six years between 1939 and 1945 and yet it was only in the closing stages of the struggle that the Royal Navy was finally receiving in sufficient quantities the types of ships and aircraft which were really suited to the operational tasks it was being called upon to perform. Not that the Navy was alone in this respect. For example, it was only in the latter half of 1944 that the RAF's Bomber Command was routinely able to hit targets accurately and in enough strength to do real damage, significantly hitting German industry and oil supplies, while the Army was in no fit state to mount an invasion of northwest Europe until the same year due to the lack of sufficient trained men and equipment.

However, the period of gestation for a warship, from initial requirement to commissioning into service, is probably longer than any other weapon system and the Royal Navy's destroyers were no exception to this. In August 1945, with VJ day marking the end of hostilities, the paper strength of the Navy's destroyer flotillas, including those manned by the Commonwealth navies, was in excess of 200 ships. During the war no less than 156 destroyers of all types (including the 'Hunt' class escort destroyers) had been built and in the dark days of 1940 another 50 old four-stackers had been obtained from the United States under the first of many Lend/Lease deals which helped to keep Britain fighting. Nevertheless, such was the ferocity of the fighting in which destroyers were involved that a total of 169 had been lost — mostly to air or submarine attacks.

Consequently, the make up of the remaining destroyer force varied considerably in quality and age. Over 100 ships had been completed before the war and had seen six years of arduous service, while over 50 of these dated from the end of World War 1. Most of the latter were of the famous 'V' and 'W' classes which had undergone a series of modifications and changes of armament in order to suit them for use as escorts to ocean convoys — a service which they performed with great distinction despite their age. More modern ships included survivors from classes 'A' to 'I' built in the 1930s, although these flotillas had been decimated; for example only one 'H' class, HMS *Hotspur*, survived a class of eight ships plus a leader.

Naturally, the coming of peace led to an immediate reduction in the numbers of ships required and these older destroyers were the first to be laid up and scrapped. In fact this process had already started before the end of hostilities, as some older ships were laid up so that their crews could provide the manpower needed for the newer

Below:
Of the nine ships of the prewar 'H' class flotilla, HMS *Hotspur* was the only one to survive the war. Shown here in 1947, she has a reduced armament and shows a typical late war colour scheme with a dark grey hull and light upperworks. She was sold to Dominica in 1948. *Maritime Photo Library*

ypes coming into service. The rapid disposal of the older destroyers has little relevance to the main theme of this book, so details of ships up to and including the 'H' and 'I' class flotillas launched up to 1939, which survived the war, will be found in Appendix 1.

In fact this is a convenient point to commence a review because the subsequent classes of destroyer were considerably larger and more heavily armed than the earlier standard prewar flotilla types. The most famous of these were the well known 'Tribal' class, followed in turn by the 'J', 'K', 'L', 'M' and 'N' classes; the postwar careers of these ships is dealt with in the following sections. In each case the class list at the head of each section refers only to those ships which survived the war.

'Tribal' Class (British) Destroyers — *Ashanti, Eskimo, Nubian, Tartar*

By the mid-1930s the Admiralty was concerned at the development of large, heavily armed destroyers by various foreign navies (particularly that of Japan). These appeared to outclass the standard British destroyer of the period as exemplified by the contemporary 'E' and 'F' classes (1,400 tons, four 4.7in guns, eight torpedo tubes, 36kt). Ultimately this led to vessels such as the French *Le Fantasque* (2,569 tons, five 5.5in guns, nine torpedo tubes, 37+kt), the Japanese *Fubuki* 'Special Type' (2,000 tons, six 5in guns, nine 24in torpedo tubes, 36kt) and the American *Porter* (1,850 tons, eight 5in guns, eight torpedo tubes, 37kt).

Although the Royal Navy was reluctant to build destroyers of this size, believing that the more traditional types met their needs, it nevertheless felt obliged to produce a suitable design so that its individual ships should not be outclassed. The result was the 'Tribal' class which were ordered in late 1935. The first group of seven were laid down the following year and ultimately a total of 16 ships were built for the Royal Navy. The original specification called for no less than 10 4.7in guns in five twin turrets, with a secondary consideration that some of these should be capable of limited AA fire by having an elevation of 40°. A torpedo armament was also called for, as was a range of 5,500 miles and a speed of 36kt — all this to be achieved within the weight limitation of 1,850 tons laid down by the Washington Treaty. From this it is obvious that surface action characteristics were to take priority, although a good close range AA armament was specified.

However, as the sketch designs progressed, the threat from the air was given more consideration and it was decided that all the main armament should have a 40° elevation. In order to provide this within the tonnage limitations and leave space for at least one multiple 2pdr pom-pom mounting, the final design featured only eight 4.7in guns and one quadruple set of torpedo tubes. A correctly anticipated shortage of gun mountings and fire control systems also helped the decision to reduce the main armament. All 16 Royal Navy ships were in service by the outbreak of war when early experience rapidly showed up several basic flaws in the philosophy of the design.

The 40° elevation of the main armament was totally useless against the dive-bombing tactics of

Below:
HMS *Cossack* entering Portsmouth in 1938 makes a striking contrast with the picture of HMS *Nubian* in 1944 reproduced overleaf. In particular *Cossack* has no radar and a negligible light AA armament.
Wright and Logan

Above:
HMS *Nubian* was one of only four survivors of the 16 British 'Tribal' class destroyers. This view shows her in 1944 while operating in the Indian Ocean. Many wartime alterations are visible including the new lattice foremast, with Types 293 and 291 radars, and the single 40mm guns in the bridge wings.
Maritime Photo Library

the Luftwaffe, while the difficulties of accurate surface gunnery from a destroyer were highlighted at the two Narvik engagements and this negated the value of mounting extra guns. As the war progressed, various steps were taken to try and solve these problems and virtually all ships of the class had X mounting removed and replaced by a twin 4in mounting still controlled by the original AA rangefinder/director installed for the other guns. The light AA armament was increased by the addition of extra 2pdr and 20mm guns as they became available, plus a few 40mm right at the end of the war for some of the surviving ships. Of these there were, sadly, only four in commission by August 1945, the rest having been sunk — *Afridi*, *Gurkha*, *Maori*, *Mashona*, and *Zulu* by air attack; *Cossack*, *Matabele* and *Somali* by U-boats; *Mohawk*, *Bedouin* and *Sikh* to a variety of surface actions while *Punjabi* was sunk in a collision with the battleship *King George V*. In fact all these losses occurred up to the autumn of 1942, dramatically illustrating the turn in the allies' fortunes after that time.

By 1945 the remaining four ships (*Ashanti*, *Eskimo*, *Nubian* and *Tartar*) formed the 10th Destroyer Flotilla and were part of the Far East Fleet (except *Ashanti* which was refitting on the Tyne) where they remained for the rest of the year engaged in various mopping up operations, before returning home to the UK in January 1946 when they were laid up in reserve.

The sum total of wartime changes can be illustrated by looking at HMS *Nubian* as she appeared in late 1945. Apart from six 4.7in and two 4in guns in twin mountings, she also carried a four-barrelled 2pdr pom-pom, two single 40mm guns between the funnels and four twin 20mm mountings — two on the after superstructure and two in the bridge wings. Her funnels were shortened to give better arcs of fire to the AA guns and a lattice mast had replaced the original tripod foremast. The latter change, of course, was necessitated by the addition of numerous radar outfits during various refits. These included a Type 293 surface/air warning set at the top of the foremast, a Type 285 gunnery radar on the Mk III(W) director and a Type 291 gunnery radar as well as various IFF equipment and HF/DF on a pole mainmast.

After being laid up in reserve, *Eskimo* was used for a while as an accommodation and base ship at Chatham while *Tartar* acted as flagship for the Senior Officer Reserve Fleet at Devonport. *Ashanti* and *Nubian* were both used in trials to test the effectiveness of various explosive devices against ship structures before being scrapped in 1949, by which time the other two ships were also being broken up.

The 'Tribal' class will always be regarded as the prewar epitome of British destroyer design with their balanced good looks and valiant wartime record. However, the fate of the British vessels is not the end of the story as several ships of the same basic design were built for the Commonwealth navies of Australia and Canada, some of the latter not being completed until well after the war.

'Tribal' Class (Australian) Destroyers — *Arunta, Bataan, Warramunga*

As war approached, the various Commonwealth navies looked at ways to expand their forces to protect their own waters and to assist the Royal Navy in its worldwide commitments. To this end both Australia and Canada each planned to commission a complete flotilla of eight 'Tribals', but in the former's case this was very soon cut back to three ships which would be built in Australia. The first of these, HMAS *Arunta*, was laid down at Sydney's Cockatoo Yard late in 1939 and was completed in 1942. The second ship, *Warramunga*, was completed a few months later but the third was not completed until May 1945. This was originally to have been named *Kurnai* but was later renamed *Bataan* to commemorate the gallant defence of that part of the Philippines by American forces in 1942, the year that she was laid down.

All three were basically identical to the British ships except that they shipped the twin 4in mounting in X position from the start and did not mount multiple machine guns as 20mm and 2pdr guns were then in plentiful supply. *Arunta* and *Warramunga* had active war careers in the South-west Pacific; the former distinguished herself by sinking a Japanese submarine and was also involved in the battle of Leyte Gulf when she took part in the Surigao Strait action. In January 1945 she was hit by a Kamikaze but was repaired to see further action.

Below:
Unlike her two sister ships, HMAS *Bataan* was not substantially altered in the postwar years. This photo shows her in the 1950s with a new lattice mast surmounted by an American air warning radar but she retains her original main armament of six 4.7in and two 4in guns, together with four 21in torpedo tubes. The multiple 2pdr aft is supplemented by six single 40mm AA guns. *Maritime Photo Library*

After the war all three ships remained active and were modified by having a lattice foremast replace the original tripod, as in the surviving RN ships. The outbreak of the Korean War saw further demand for their services in support of the United Nations forces ashore. However, with the stabilisation of the situation in 1951-52 *Arunta* and *Warramunga* were withdrawn for modernisation refits. The after 4.7in mounting was removed and replaced by a Squid AS mortar and the light AA armament was completely revised to consist of six single 40mm Bofors Mk 7 mountings and a Mk 5 twin 40mm with its associated STD which replaced the original multiple 2pdr mounting. The single guns were carried in the bridge wings, between the funnels, and on the after superstructure, although the latter pair were later removed as they interfered with the arcs of fire of the Mk 5 twin. The quadruple 21in torpedo tube mounting amidships was retained.

The electronics fit was updated, Types 170 and 174 sonars were fitted to complement the Squid mortar, and Types 293Q air/surface warning radar was fitted at the masthead with a Type 974 navigation radar below. The original HA director with Type 985 gunnery radar was retained, as was HF/DF on a pole extension to the foremast.

Arunta was the first to be modernised, work commencing in 1951, while *Warramunga's* refit took place between November 1952 and October 1954, after which she remained in service until being laid up in 1960 along with her sister ship. *Bataan* was scheduled for a similar conversion but the work was never carried out. Being completed later than the others, she was fitted with a light AA armament of six 40mm guns as well as the multiple 2pdr and also received an American SC or SA series radar. For service in Korea the 2pdr was replaced by a Mk 5 twin Bofors but otherwise she was substantially unaltered. She was finally paid off into reserve in 1956 and was scrapped in 1962.

'Tribal' Class (Canadian) Destroyers — *Haida, Huron, Iroquois, Cayuga, Micmac, Nookta, Athabaskan* (ii)

Like Australia, Canada also decided to order a full flotilla of eight 'Tribals' at the outbreak of war. However, in this case the full quota of eight ships was finally completed. Of these, four were built by Vickers Armstrong on the Tyne while the others were built in Canada. Only the British-built ships were completed in time for war service and one of these, the original *Athabaskan*, was sunk off the northwest French coast in April 1944. As completed, the first four ships (*Athabaskan, Haida, Huron, Iroquois*) differed from the British 'Tribals' in that the quad 2pdr was mounted high up on the after superstructure to give better arcs of fire and all were fitted with at least six single 20mm guns. By the end of the war the three survivors had new lattice masts with Type 293 radar, and a Mk III(W) director which controlled both high and low-angle gunnery. Employed in European waters throughout the war, the three ships finally arrived in Canada in late 1945.

The four Canadian-built ships (*Micmac, Nookta, Cayuga,* and a second *Athabaskan*) were actually built as two separate pairs. The first two were generally similar to the Tyne-built ships but *Cayuga* and *Athabaskan* were completed in 1947 and 1948 to a substantially altered configuration which took advantage of war experience and the availability of new equipment. The main armament now consisted of eight 4in AA guns in four twin mountings with RPC, controlled by a Mk 6 director, while the quad 2pdr was replaced by Mk 5 twin Bofors with a further four single 40mm guns around the bridge and funnels.

The seven Canadian 'Tribals' saw considerable postwar service — several operating off Korea —

and all underwent substantial modernisations. In the early 1950s the Tyne-built ships were altered by the removal of the original 4.7in guns and their replacement by twin 4in mountings in A and B positions, the Y mount having already been removed to make way for a Squid AS mortar. AA armament was rationalised to a combination of single and twin 40mm mountings. This brought all

Below:
HMCS *Huron* was one of four 'Tribal' class built in Britain for the RCN. After many refits and modernisations her final outline was as shown with twin 4in guns forward and a twin 3in AA aft. Both installations have their own Mk 63 fire control system with a target tracking radar on B mounting and another on the 3in mounting. Note also the Squid mortars aft. *Real Photos (N850)*

Right:
This close up of HMCS *Athabaskan* off Korea shows the single 40mm guns abreast the funnel and in the bridge wings. At the after end of the bridge is the Mk VI fire control director with the Type 275 radar nacelles on either side. The Mk VI equipped many British destroyers in the immediate postwar era. *Imperial War Museum*

Below right:
HMCS *Cayuga* was one of the Canadian-built 'Tribals' and retained her Mk VI director throughout her career. A new lattice mast supports a US SPS-10 radar but a British Type 293Q is at the very top of the polemast extension. *Real Photos (N851)*

seven ships into roughly the same layout. However, further modernisations in the mid-1950s led to a final armament of two twin 4in AA mountings forward and an American pattern twin 3in AA in X position. The 3in mounting — originally open, but later enclosed in a fibreglass gunshield — incorporated its own Mk 63 fire control system. This was also adopted for the 4in guns forward in some cases, with the gunnery radar attached to B mounting while others retained the Mk 6 director. Other noticeable modifications included new, heavier lattice masts to carry an increasing array of radars (mostly of American pattern), raked funnel cowls which considerably altered their appearance, and the extension of the after deckhouse to provide extra accommodation. Although by this period the ships were functioning as fleet escorts rather than as traditional destroyers, they still retained the quadruple torpedo tubes amidships. All seven paid off into reserve between 1960 and 1964 and were subsequently scrapped with the notable exeception of HMCS *Haida* which was preserved and can currently be seen as a museum ship at Toronto — the lone survivor of a famous class of fighting ship.

Name	No	Laid Down	Launched	Completed	Builder	Yard	Remarks	
Nubian	G36	10/08/36	21/12/37	06/12/38	Thornycroft	Woolston	Arr Briton Ferry for scrap	25/06/49
Ashanti	G51	23/11/36	05/11/37	21/12/38	Denny	Dunbarton	Arr Troon for scrap	12/04/49
Eskimo	G75	05/08/36	03/09/37	30/12/38	Vickers Armstrong	Tyne	Arr Troon for scrap	27/06/49
Tartar	G43	26/08/36	21/10/37	10/03/39	Swan Hunter	Tyne	Arr Newport for scrap	22/12/48
Arunta (RAN)	D130	15/11/39	30/10/40	03/03/42	Cockatoo	Australia	Sank en route Japan for scrap	13/02/69
Warramunga (RAN)	D123	10/02/40	06/02/42	23/11/42	Cockatoo	Australia	Scrapped Japan	1963
Bataan (RAN)	D191	18/02/42	15/01/44	25/05/45	Cockatoo	Australia	Scrapped Japan	1962
Iroquois (RCN)	217	19/09/40	23/09/41	10/12/42	Vickers Armstrong	Tyne	Arr Bilbao, Spain, for scrap	09/66
Huron (RCN)	216	15/07/41	25/06/42	28/07/43	Vickers Armstrong	Tyne	Arr La Spezia, Italy, for scrap	28/05/65
Haida (RCN)	215	29/09/41	25/08/42	18/09/43	Vickers Armstrong	Tyne	Museum Ship, Toronto	1964
Micmac (RCN)	214	20/05/42	18/09/43	14/09/45	Halifax Shipyard	Halifax	Arr Faslane for scrap	09/64
Nookta (RCN)	213	20/05/42	26/04/44	08/10/46	Halifax Shipyard	Halifax	Arr Faslane for scrap	06/10/64
Cayuga (RCN)	218	07/10/43	28/07/45	20/10/47	Halifax Shipyard	Halifax	Arr Faslane for scrap	06/10/64
Athabaskan (RCN)	219	15/05/44	14/05/46	20/02/48	Halifax Shipyard	Halifax	Scrapped	1970

Data:	'Tribal' class, HMS *Nubian* (1945)
Displacement (tons):	1,960 standard, 2,520 full load
Length/Beam (ft):	377 (oa)/36.5
Draught (ft):	9 (light), 14 (full load)
Armament:	3×twin 4.7in, 1×twin 4in HA Mk XIX mounting, 1×quadruple 2pdr, 2×single 40mm, 4×twin 20mm, 4×21in torpedo tubes (1×4), 2×depth charge throwers
Radars:	Types 285, 291, 293
Machinery:	3×Admiralty 3-drum boilers (300lb/sq in/620°F), 2×shafts, Parsons geared turbines, 44,000shp
Speed/Range:	32kt/5,700nm @ 15kt
Oil Fuel (tons):	525
Complement:	220

Data:	'Tribal' class, HMCS *Cayuga* (1962)
Displacement (tons):	2,200 standard, 2,800 full load
Length/Beam (ft):	377 (oa)/36.5
Draught (ft):	9.5 (light), 15 (full load)
Armament:	2×twin 4in AA Mk XIX mountings, 1×twin 3in/50cal, 4×single 40mm, 2×Squid AS mortars

Radars:	SPS-6, Types 275, 262 (gunnery)
Machinery:	3×Admiralty 3-drum boilers (300lb/sq in/620°F), 2×shafts, Parsons geared turbines, 44,000shp
Speed/range:	32kt/3,400nm @ 20kt
Oil Fuel (tons):	520
Complement:	240

Data:	'Tribal' class, HMAS *Arunta* (1955)
Displacement (tons):	2,012 standard, 2,700 full load
Length/Beam (ft):	377 (oa)/36.5
Draught (ft):	13.5 (mean)
Armament:	4×4.7in on 2×CP Mk XIX mountings, 1×twin 4in AA, 8×40mm (1× twin, 6×single), 4×21in torpedo tubes, Squid AS mortar
Radars:	Types 293, 285
Machinery:	3×Admiralty 3-drum boilers, 2×shafts, Parsons geared turbines, 44,000shp
Speed/Range:	32kt
Oil Fuel (tons):	525
Complement:	293

'J', 'K' and 'N' Class Destroyers — *Jervis, Javelin, Kelvin, Kimberley, Napier, Nerissa, Nizam, Noble, Nonpareil, Norman, Nepal*

The 'J' class destroyers were ordered in March 1937 under the 1936 Defence Estimates and were intended as a follow on from the 'Tribal' class which would be both smaller and more suitable for general fleet duties. The head of the destroyer section of the Constructor's Department was A. P. Cole who had designed the 'Tribal' class and had several new ideas which he wanted to see incorporated into British destroyer design. These included the adoption of a two-boiler layout (as opposed to the three which the Naval Staff insisted on as the minimum for battle damage survivability) which would lead to a single funnel and hence reduce the silhouette and improve AA fire arcs, the retention of the twin 4.7in mounting as standard for fleet destroyers, and the adoption of a system of longitudinal framing to ease construction while increasing strength. In the event, with the help of some lobbying behind the scenes by Lord Louis Mountbatten, who took a personal interest in the design work, the new ships incorporated all these features and proved to be handsome and popular vessels. In particular, the hull design and machinery layout proved to be very successful and was, as will be seen, perpetuated in several succeeding destroyer designs.

Under the policy started with the 'Tribals', the standard flotilla of these large destroyers was to consist of eight ships — one of which would be fitted out as a leader. The eight 'J' class were therefore laid down in 1937, followed by eight identical 'K' class in 1937-38 and finally another eight 'N' class in 1939-40. This made a total of 24 ships and, like the 'Tribals', they were involved in the bloodiest fighting and consequently suffered heavy losses, particularly among the 'J' and 'K' classes which were all in service by 1940. By 1945 only *Jervis, Javelin, Kelvin* and *Kimberley* survived, while the 'N' class, which generally did not commission until 1941, were more fortunate and only lost one ship (*Nestor*, 1942).

As originally completed, the 'J' and 'K' classes displaced 1,760 tons (standard), were just over 350ft long, and were armed with six 4.7in guns in three twin mounts, one quad 2pdr pom-pom and 10 21in torpedo tubes. In fact, apart from being 20ft shorter and lacking the extra 4.7in mounting, they were not much different to the 'Tribals' in overall effectiveness. The advantage of the heavier torpedo armament was soon lost as the after bank of tubes was quickly replaced by a HA 4in AA gun. Later war modifications included increased light AA armament and the addition of various radars as they became available. By 1945 *Jervis* and *Javelin* had a light AA armament of six 20mm guns to supplement the multiple 2pdr, the 4in gun had been removed so that the original torpedo tubes could be replaced, and a new lattice foremast was fitted. Radar outfit included Type 293 air/surface warning, Type 285 on the gunnery director, and HF/DF on a pole mainmast. The two remaining 'K' class ships were similarly fitted.

At the end of the war *Javelin*, *Jervis* and *Kelvin* were operating in home waters while *Kimberley* was in the Mediterranean. Both of the 'Ks' were quickly decommissioned and laid up in January 1946. They were later used in various target trials before being scrapped in 1949. *Jervis* and *Javelin* saw a little more service, operating in the Eastern Mediterranean in 1946 before returning home and paying off into reserve. They also suffered the indignity of being used in the target trials of the late 1940s before being scrapped.

The 'N' class were generally completed as the earlier ships except that they shipped a 4in gun instead of the after bank of torpedo tubes, were fitted with some single 20mm guns and were radar equipped (Type 286 air warning and Type 285 gunnery set) from the start. However their naming and allocation was rather confusing and they were never employed as a homogeneous flotilla. HMS *Norseman* was under construction at Woolston when she was heavily damaged during an air raid so that her completion was delayed until well into 1942, by which time she had been renamed *Nepal* and was destined to be the only ship of the class to be British manned during the war. Of the others, *Napier*, *Nestor*, *Nizam*, and *Norman* were transferred to the RAN on completion, while *Noble* and *Nonpareil* were handed over to the Royal Netherlands Navy and renamed *Van Galen* and *Tjerk Hiddes* respectively. Finally *Nerissa* was Polish manned and renamed *Piorun*. With the loss of *Nestor*, *Nepal* appears to have also been transferred to the RAN, and by 1945 all the Dutch and Australian manned ships were serving in the Far East, *Napier* actually being present at the Japanese surrender ceremonies held in Tokyo Bay in September 1945.

After the war, the Australian ships were returned to the Royal Navy, arriving back in the UK by the end of 1945 and going straight into reserve, seeing no further service. The single exception to this was HMS *Nepal* which was refitted with a reduced armament and used as an AS trials ship until 1949 when she finally paid off. The Polish manned *Piorun* was not officially returned to the Royal Navy until September 1946 when she was renamed *Noble* and passed into reserve.

The two Dutch ships had a more active postwar career, both seeing action in the fighting in the Netherlands East Indies before the emergence of an independent Indonesia. In 1949 they returned to the Netherlands and underwent refits at Den Helder following which the *Tjerk Hiddes* was transferred to the Indonesian Navy in 1951 and renamed (yet again) *Gadjah Mada*, remaining in service for many years until being scrapped in 1961. *Van Galen* returned to Far East waters after her refit in 1951 and spent nearly 12 months operating as part of the United Nations forces off Korea. She finally paid off at home in 1956 and was scrapped the following year.

Data: 'N' class, HMS *Norman* (1945)
Displacement (tons): 1,770 standard, 2,380 full load
Length/Beam (ft): 356½ (oa)/35¾
Draught (ft): 9 (light), 13½ (full load)
Armament: 6×4.7in guns on 3×CP Mk XIX twin mountings, 1×quadruple 2pdr, 1×40mm, 10×20mm AA guns, 8×21in TT (2×4)
Radars: Types 291AW, 285
Machinery: 2×Admiralty 3-drum boilers (300lb/sq in/620°F), 2×shafts, Parsons geared turbines, 40,000shp
Speed/Range: 32kt/5,500nm @ 15kt
Oil Fuel (tons): 491
Complement: 220

Name	No	Laid Down	Launched	Completed	Builder	Yard	Remarks	
Jervis	G00		09/09/38		Hawthorn Leslie	Hebburn	Arr Troon for scrap	03/01/49
Javelin	G61		21/12/38		J. Brown	Clydebank	Arr Troon for scrap	11/49
Kelvin	G37	05/10/37	19/01/39	27/10/39	Fairfield	Govan	Arr Troon for scrap	06/49
Kimberley	G50	17/01/38	01/06/39	21/12/39	Thornycroft	Woolston	Arr Troon for scrap	30/03/49
Napier	D297	26/07/39	22/05/40	11/12/40	Fairfield	Govan	Arr Briton Ferry for scrap	17/01/56
Nerissa	D165	26/07/39	07/05/40	04/11/40	J. Brown	Clydebank	*Noble* (1946). Scrapped Dunston	12/55
Nizam	D38	27/07/39	04/07/40	08/01/41	J. Brown	Clydebank	Arr Grays, Essex, for scrap	16/11/55
Noble	G84	10/07/39	17/04/41	20/02/42	Denny	Dunbarton	RNethN *Van Galen* 1942. B/Up	08/02/57
Nonpareil	G16	22/05/40	25/06/41	30/10/42	Denny	Dunbarton	RNethN/Indonesia N. Scrapped	1961
Norman	D149	27/07/39	30/10/40	29/09/41	Thornycroft	Woolston	Arr Newport for scrap	01/04/58
Nepal	D125	09/09/39	04/12/41	29/05/42	Thornycroft	Woolston	Arr Briton Ferry for scrap	16/01/56

'L' and 'M' Class Destroyers — *Lookout, Loyal, Marne, Matchless, Meteor, Musketeer, Milne*

As originally designed, these ships were undoubtedly the best of the prewar destroyer designs and were fully the equal of contemporary

Left:
A rare photo showing the Polish-manned *Piorun* at Plymouth in 1946. Originally laid down as HMS *Nerissa*, she was handed over to the Polish Navy on completion and returned to the Royal Navy in 1946 when she was renamed HMS *Noble*. Note the 4in gun still carried in lieu of the after torpedo tubes. *Husbands Camera Centre*

Bottom left:
HMS *Lookout* was the only 'L' class destroyer in service at the end of the war, the others having been sunk or written off. She is shown laid up at Devonport and the Mk XX twin 4.7in gun mounting can be clearly seen on the after superstructure. Also of interest is the Type 271 radar lantern amidships. *Maritime Photo Library*

Below:
HMS *Marne* enters Malta in December 1945. She still wears her wartime camouflage and light AA armament consists of four twin 20mm guns and a quadruple 2pdr. A lattice foremast carries Type 271 and 291 radars. *Wright and Logan*

ships in other navies. Originally they were intended to have a speed of around 40kt to counter the rising speeds of the contemporary fast battleships. However, to meet the installed power requirements to reach this speed would have entailed a step-up in size to a standard displacement of over 2,500 tons which was regarded at the time as being completely unacceptable. In consequence the result was a slightly enlarged 'J' class design with an extra 8,000shp to maintain 36kt and equipped with a new Mk XX twin 4.7in mounting in a totally enclosed gunhouse replacing the CP XIX mounting of the 'Tribal' and 'J' class. The new mounting was a significant improvement as it allowed the guns to be elevated to 50° and the gun crews were completely protected from the elements, thus improving their performance in adverse weather conditions. The 4.7in gun was also a new model (QF Mk XI) which fired a 62lb shell compared with the standard 50lb shell of the earlier Mk IX/XII carried by earlier destroyers. Maximum range was also increased, from 16,970yd to over 21,000yd. The individual guns could be elevated separately but the whole mounting could not be considered a true turret as the ammunition supply was by means of a fixed hoist which did not rotate with the mounting and this could cause problems at extreme angles of training. The layout

of the ammunition supply dictated the wide spacing of the guns which gave the mounting its distinctive and imposing appearance. To go with the new guns was an improved fire control system — a Mk IV Type TP combined HA/LA director.

The eight ships of the 'L' class flotilla were authorised under the 1937 Estimates and laid down during 1938-39. However, problems with the supply of the new gun mountings led to a decision to rearm four of the ships (*Lance*, *Larne*, *Legion* and *Lively*) with eight 4in AA guns in four twin mountings in order to expedite their introduction into service. In 1940 HMS *Larne* was renamed *Gurkha* following the loss of the 'Tribal' class destroyer of that name. The other four ships were eventually completed to the original design except that the after bank of torpedo tubes was replaced by a single 4in gun as even the 50° elevation of the new 4.7in mounting was still not sufficient to deal with enemy dive-bombing tactics. All eight ships also carried a multiple 2pdr mounting abaft the single funnel and were completed with a variety of other light AA weapons.

Unfortunately, consideration of the postwar history of these ships is a simple matter as all except *Lookout* were lost to enemy action. *Loyal* was mined off Italy in 1944 and was written off as a total loss, but was towed home and not actually scrapped until 1948. After the end of the war *Lookout* paid off into reserve almost immediately and was scrapped in 1948.

By comparison, the 'M' class generally had a longer and more interesting postwar career. Of the eight ships ordered in 1939, all except *Marksman* were in service by 1942. The latter was almost destroyed in an air raid while on the slipway during 1941 and a new hull was laid down later that year. By the time of her completion in August 1943 she had been renamed *Mahratta*, perhaps one of the Navy's unluckiest ships as she was quickly sunk by a U-boat in February 1944 after less than six months in commission. *Martin* and *Myrmidon* (transferred to the Polish Navy and renamed *Orkan*) were also lost, but the other five ships survived the war. At the end of the war they operated in the Aegean in support of operations against Axis forces still fighting in that area, before returning home and paying off into reserve early in 1946 in common with many other surviving destroyers which had no peacetime employment. However, they were not forgotten and all except *Marne* received a refit in 1950-51 and at various times they were used as accommodation or static training ships. At the end of the war all ships had a

Below:
Entering Portsmouth in April 1946 with a paying off pennant at the masthead, HMS *Matchless* has a Type 291 radar at the masthead with a Type 293 below, while the HF/DF is on the polemast aft.
Wright and Logan

attice mast carrying Type 293 and 272 radars except *Musketeer* which retained her tripod foremast until the 1950 refit) and carried a full complement of eight torpedo tubes.

During the late 1940s the role of various ships and the future structure of the fleet was the subject of considerable debate. It was accepted that the Navy's major offensive weapon against surface targets was the carrier-based aircraft and that the destroyer would thus have little scope for traditional torpedo attacks. Consequently the concept of a Fast Fleet Escort grew up which required the characteristics of high speed, good seakeeping ability, and an effective anti-aircraft and anti-submarine armament. As will be seen, this requirement was met by the various modifications to other destroyer classes, but as an extension of this policy a further requirement arose for ships which would carry long-range radars capable of giving early warning of air attacks and be fitted with the facilities to direct the ensuing air battle. Such ships would also be needed to accompany convoys as well as task forces, and for this purpose several frigate projects based on converted destroyer hulls were proposed.

One of these was the Type 62 air defence frigate which, armed with twin 4in and twin 40mm gun mountings, would carry two each of the Type 982/983 long range air warning and height finding radars. In 1950 it was proposed that the five 'M' class and seven other later 'Emergency' class be converted in this way. It soon became apparent that only the larger 'M' class would be able to support the full range of radar outfits proposed and would be better employed as fast air defence escorts for carrier task forces. Apart from the new radars and armament, the conversion would entail an extension of the forecastle deck to increase internal volume and the provision of extra diesel generators to meet the necessary electrical power requirements.

A review of fleet requirements together with a major cost cutting exercise in 1954 resulted in the cancellation of the Type 62 project. However, the requirement for ships of this type remained and would eventually be met by other destroyer conversions.

M Class Destroyers Transferred to Turkey

Ship	New Name/No	Transfer Date
Marne	D351 *Maresal Fevsi Cakmak*	9/6/59
Matchless	D350 *Kilic Ali Pasha*	16/7/59
Meteor	D348 *Piyale Pasha*	29/6/59
Milne	D349 *Alp Arslam*	27/4/59

Below:
HMS *Milne* under tow prior to being refitted for sale to Turkey. She still retains her full torpedo armament but the main armament and Mk V director are cocooned. *Skyfotos*

Above:
HMS *Marne*, one of four 'M' class destroyers sold to Turkey in 1959, was renamed *Maresal Fevsi Cakmak* and is shown flying the Turkish flag after transfer. Note the ESM equipment and the Type 293Q radar on the foremast. The after deckhouse has been enlarged to carry two Squid mortars and one set of torpedo tubes has been landed.
Maritime Photo Library

Musketeer was subsequently scrapped the following year, but the other four (*Marne, Matchless, Meteor* and *Milne*) were sold to Turkey under an agreement signed in Ankara on 16 August 1957, and were taken out of reserve to be refitted over the next two years. Among the changes made were the replacement of the previous light AA armament by a Mk V twin 40mm Bofors mounting abaft the funnel and four single 40mm in the bridge wings and amidships. The after torpedo tubes were replaced by a deckhouse carrying a Squid AS mortar and the sonar and radar outfits were updated. In this form the ships were commissioned into the Turkish Navy in 1959 under their new names (see table on page 29) which commemorated famous generals and admirals. All four remained in service until the early 1970s when they were laid up for disposal.

Thus the last of the big prewar destroyers passed away, having played little part in the postwar Royal Navy. The 'M' class in particular appeared to have potential for modernisation and continued use, but one major factor which weighed against all these ships was the vulnerability of their turbine castings to shock damage. Improved metallurgical techniques made the later ships less susceptible and this was one reason for the early demise of many destroyers of prewar design.

Name	No	Laid Down	Launched	Completed	Builder	Yard	Remarks	
Lookout	G32		04/11/40		Scotts	Greenock	Arr Newport for scrap	29/02/48
Milne	D58	24/01/40	30/12/41	06/08/42	Scotts/J. Brown	Greenock	Turkish Navy 1959. For disposal	1971
Marne	D135	23/10/39	30/10/40	02/12/41	Vickers Armstrong	Tyne	Turkish Navy 1959. For disposal	1971
Matchless	D252	14/09/40	04/09/41	26/04/42	Alex Stephen	Linthouse	Turkish Navy 1959. For disposal	1971
Meteor	D273	14/09/40	03/11/41	12/08/42	Alex Stephen	Linthouse	Turkish Navy 1959. Laid up	1972
Musketeer	D186	07/12/39	02/12/41	18/09/42	Fairfield	Govan	Arr Sunderland for scrap	06/12/55

Data:	'M' class, HMS *Matchless* (1946)	**Radars:**	Types 293 GW, 291 AW, 285
Displacement (tons):	1,920 standard, 2,725 full load	**Machinery:**	2×Admiralty 3-drum boilers
Length/Beam (ft):	362.5 (oa)/37		(300lb/sq in/660°F), 2×shafts,
Draught (ft):	10 (light), 14.5 (full load)		Parsons SR geared turbines,
Armament:	6×4.7in guns on 3×twin Mk XX		48,000shp
	mountings, 1×Mk VII quadruple	**Speed/Range:**	32.5kt/5,500nm @ 12kt
	2pdr, 8×20mm AA, 8×21in	**Oil Fuel** (tons):	567
	torpedo tubes (2×4)	**Complement:**	200

2 Conversions and Disposals

Although the destroyers, both large and small, which had been designed immediately prior to 1939 turned out to have little part to play in the postwar Navy, the same was not true of the numerous Emergency Programme destroyers which were laid down from 1940 onwards in ever increasing numbers. These consisted of the 16 ships of the 'O' and 'P' classes, another 16 of the 'Q' and 'R' classes, and no less than six full flotillas of the 'S' to 'Z' classes. As most of these were commissioned from 1942 onwards, when the

Allied cause was beginning to prosper, their losses were considerably lighter and consequently no less than 70 ships survived the war. Although some remained in service as conventional destroyers, most were either converted to fast AS frigates or sold abroad — some already having been transferred during the war and remaining with their respective navies. It will be convenient to consider each flotilla in turn to follow the postwar career of these ships.

'O' and 'P' Class Destroyers — *Onslow, Obdurate, Obedient, Offa, Onslaught, Opportune, Oribi, Orwell, Paladin, Penn, Petard*

The design of these ships was actually prepared prior to 1939 when they were officially designated as an 'Intermediate Type' and represented a reversion to the general purpose fleet destroyer — smaller than the 'Tribals' and successive classes, but larger amd more capable than the 'Hunt' class escort destroyers also under construction. Staff requirements were for a vessel of 1,500 tons utilising the basic 'J' class hull and machinery but carrying only four single 4.7in guns, eight torpedo tubes and a light AA armament including a multiple 2pdr mounting. Apart from the single tunnel, these ships were to be similar in outline to the earlier 'A' to 'I' classes, and as completed, the hull was some 10ft shorter than that of the 'J' class.

The 'O' class flotilla was actually ordered on 3 September 1939, the day that war broke out, and a repeat order for eight similar 'P' class ships followed on 20 October. All 16 were laid down in late 1939 or 1940 and all were in service by 1942. The experience of early war actions together with a shortage of 4.7in guns and fire control equipment led to a major revision of armament layout in some ships and the completion of others was delayed. In

Below:
All eight ships of the 'P' class were completed with a main armament of five 4in guns as illustrated by this wartime view of HMS *Penn*. *Real Photos (S1593)*

order to meet the threat of air attack, some of the class would be completed with a main gun armament of five 4in AA in single mountings and only one quadruple set of torpedo tubes.

In order to maintain two homogeneous flotillas it was decided that eight ships would be completed as originally designed and form the 'O' class, while the remaining eight would form the 'P' class flotilla with the revised armament layout. This resulted in some confusing swopping of names among ships already laid down and, in general, the 'P' class were completed earlier than the sister flotilla. To add to the confusion, four of the 'O' class (*Obdurate*, *Obedient*, *Opportune*, *Orwell*) were modified to act as minelayers, being fitted to carry 60 mines if required. In order to maintain stability with a full load of mines, the main armament was changed to four 4in guns and Y gun and both sets of torpedo tubes had to be removed on the occasions when mines were carried.

The 'O' class were retained for Home Fleet duties throughout the war and, surprisingly, all survived. On the other hand the 'P' class, with their better AA armament, were dispatched to the Mediterranean where four were lost up to 1943. After refitting, the remaining four joined the Far East Fleet in 1944 where *Pathfinder* was bombed and written off in 1945. However, the hull was towed home and used as a target before being scrapped in 1948. Another partial survivor was *Porcupine* which was torpedoed by a U-boat in 1942 and broke in two. The two halves were salvaged and towed to Plymouth where they were used as accommodation hulks (known as *Pork* and *Pine*) until 1947.

During her 1944 refit, *Penn's* main armament layout was altered to two twin Mk XIX 4in mountings (in B and X positions) to replace the previous single mountings. Radars included Types 293, 291 and 285. This was a much more effective disposition for AA fire but time did not permit similar alterations being made to other ships.

In the immediate postwar years, one of the first disposals was HMS *Oribi* which, in 1946, was transferred to the Turkish Navy and renamed *Gayret*. This was as reparation for HMS *Ithuriel*, a destroyer building for Turkey and requisitioned in 1939, subsequently being written off after a bombing attack in 1942. The other ships were kept fairly busy in the late 1940s, mostly based at Portsmouth and acting as target, training and trials ships. Generally they were stripped of much of their armament; *Offa*, for instance, carried only two 4.7in guns and B and X positions and was stripped of all other weapons while acting as an AS target ship out of Devonport in 1946/47. *Onslaught* was similarly configured except that she carried single 20mm guns in the bridge wings while employed as a submarine tender from Portsmouth in 1946. In 1945 the remaining 4.7in gun-equipped ship, *Onslow*, acted as HQ ship for Operation 'Deadlight' which involved the towing and scuttling of large numbers of surrendered U-boats gathered in Loch Ryan. After a period in reserve, she acted as a Portsmouth based target and trials ship.

In 1949 *Onslow* and *Offa* were handed over to the Pakistan Navy and renamed *Tippu Sultan* and *Tariq* respectively. Two years later *Onslaught* was also transferred and renamed *Tughril*, all three ships being refitted and rearmed with four 4.7in and six 40mm guns as well as two quadruple sets of torpedo tubes before their handover. The *Tariq* (ex-*Offa*) was returned to the Royal Navy in 1959 and scrapped the same year, but the other two were converted to Type 16 frigates in the UK between 1957-59 and survived into the late 1970s before being scrapped.

Of the 4in-armed ships, *Opportune*, *Obdurate* and *Obedient* were also variously employed on local flotilla duties and were generally little altered. *Obedient* and *Obdurate* appeared at the 1953 Coronation Review and at that time the latter carried four 4in guns, a quadruple 2pdr abaft the funnel, and single 40mm guns in the bridge wings. The torpedo tubes had been removed although she was still fitted for minelaying (indeed the two were retained in the postwar fleet specifically for their minelaying capability). All three ships were laid up between 1950 and 1955, and subsequently scrapped. The odd man out was *Orwell* which, in 1952, was converted to a Type 16 AS frigate and was active until 1958. After a refit she was placed in reserve in 1960 and later scrapped.

Of the three remaining active 'P' class ships, *Paladin* was in UK waters at the end of the war and was employed as a submarine target ship until

Above:
Orwell, Paladin and *Petard* were converted to
Type 16 frigates in 1952-54. This is HMS *Petard* and
points of note are the twin 4in mounting forward,
twin Squid aft, 40mm AA guns, and Type 293Q radar
at the masthead. *Wright and Logan*

Above right:
HMS *Obedient* was one of the ships at the 1953
Coronation Review. At that time she was based at
Chatham and was equipped for minelaying. The

mine rails can be clearly seen on the upper deck and
the discharge chutes on the stern. Although 40mm
guns have been mounted in the bridge wings, the
multiple 2pdr is still carried abaft the funnel.
Skyfotos

Right:
HMS *Orwell* in 1953. Although converted to a
Type 16 frigate, some of her 40mm guns and the
Squids have been landed to allow the ship to act as a
minelayer. *Skyfotos*

Below right:
Four of the 'O' class were completed with a main
armament of four 4.7in guns. One of these was HMS
Onslow which was sold to Pakistan in 1949 and
renamed *Tippu Sultan*. She is shown at Malta in
1951. *Wright and Logan*

being laid up in reserve in 1948. *Penn* and *Petard*
were in the Far East, the latter returning home in
late 1946 and paying off into reserve. *Penn* did not
return until the end of 1947 when she was placed in
reserve and stripped of much of her armament,
before being scrapped in 1950.

Petard and *Paladin* were both converted to
Type 16 frigates in the early 1950s as part of a
major programme to boost the Royal Navy's tally
of fast AS frigates to combat the rising strength of
the Soviet submarine fleet. Like the remaining 'O'
class, the two conversions retained their minelaying capability. Details of the Type 16 programme
are given under the section dealing with the 'T'
class destroyers. At this point it is sufficient to note
that the Type 16 was very much a stop-gap
measure and the two 'P' class ships converted
spent much of their subsequent careers in reserve
before being scrapped in the mid-1960s.

Data:	'O' class, HMS *Obedient* (1953)
Displacement (tons):	1,610 standard, 2,220 full load
Length/Beam (ft):	345 (oa)/35
Draught (ft):	9 (light), 13.5 (full load)
Armament:	3×4in QF Mk V on single Mk III** mountings, 1×Mk VII quadruple 2pdr, 3×single 40mm AA, rails for 60 mines
Radars:	Types 293, 974, 285
Machinery:	2×Admiralty 3-drum boilers (300lb/sq in/620°F), 2×shafts, Parsons geared turbines, 40,000shp
Speed/Range:	33kt/3,850nm @ 20kt
Oil Fuel (tons):	500
Complement:	170

Name	No	Laid Down	Launched	Completed	Builder	Yard	Remarks	
Obdurate	D139	25/04/40	19/02/42	03/09/42	Denny	Dunbarton	Arr Inverkeithing for scrap	30/11/64
Obedient	D248	22/05/40	30/04/42	30/10/42	Denny	Dunbarton	Arr Blyth for scrap	19/10/62
Offa	D129	15/01/40	11/03/41	20/09/41	Fairfield	Govan	PN (1949). Arr Sunderland for scrap	13/10/59
Onslaught	D04	14/01/41	09/10/41	19/06/42	Fairfield	Govan	PN (1949). Sold off for scrap	1977
Onslow	D49	01/07/40	31/03/41	08/10/41	J. Brown	Clydebank	PN (1949). Sold for scrap	1980
Opportune	D180	28/03/40	21/01/42	14/08/42	Thornycroft	Woolston	Arr Milford Haven for scrap	25/11/55
Oribi	G66	15/01/40	14/01/41	05/07/41	Fairfield	Govan	TURK N *Gayret* (1946). Scrapped	1965
Orwell	D198	20/05/40	02/04/42	17/10/42	Thornycroft	Woolston	Type 16. Arr Newport for scrap	28/06/65
Paladin	D69	22/07/40	11/06/41	12/12/41	J. Brown	Clydebank	Type 16. Arr Dunston for scrap	25/10/62
Penn	G77	26/12/39	12/02/41	23/02/42	Vickers Armstrong	Tyne	Arr Troon for scrap	31/01/50
Petard	D56	26/12/39	27/03/41	14/06/42	Vickers Armstrong	Tyne	Type 16. Arr Bo'ness for scrap	06/67

'Q' and 'R' Class Destroyers — *Quilliam, Quadrant, Quality, Queenborough, Quiberon, Quickmatch, Rotherham, Racehorse, Raider, Rapid, Redoubt, Relentless, Rocket, Roebuck*

These 16 ships were similar in concept to the previous class, but reverted to the original dimensions of the 'J' class hull and used the, by now, standard machinery arrangement of two Admiralty three-drum boilers giving an output of 40,000shp through two shafts driven by Parsons geared turbines. Designed armament was four 4.7in guns, a quadruple 2pdr, six 20mm AA and eight 21in torpedo tubes. With a reduced armament compared to the 'J' class, there was extra internal space which was used to increase bunkerage and fit extra equipment. All ships were fitted with Type 291 Air Warning radar at the top of the tripod foremast and Type 285 on the HA/LA Director.

Of the 'Q' class, *Quail* and *Quentin* were war losses. On completion, *Quiberon*, *Quickmatch* and *Quality* were transferred to the Australian Navy, while *Quadrant* and *Queenborough* were also transferred in 1945. The latter arrangement coincided with the return of the three 'N' class destroyers (qv) from Australia at the end of the war and gave the RAN a homogeneous group of ships. Officially these ships were only on loan, but ownership was formally transferred in 1950 at which time it was announced that all five would be converted to Type 15 frigates. In the event, *Quality* was not converted and was listed for disposal in 1957, being scrapped the following year. The others underwent rebuilding between 1950 and 1957 but *Quadrant* was laid up in 1962, although the remainder gave good service until the late 1960s when they were progressively replaced by the Australian-built Type 12 'River' class frigates.

Quilliam was the only other survivor of the class in 1945 when she was transferred to the Royal Netherlands Navy and renamed *Banckert*. Sub-

sequently she sailed for the Netherlands East Indies where she remained until 1948 and during this period visited Australia where she was temporarily reunited with her flotilla mates. On transfer in 1945 she bore the pennant number JT1 but this was later changed to D801 to conform with the standard NATO practice. Paid off in 1956, she was scrapped the following year.

The 'R' class all survived the war during which they formed the 24th Destroyer Flotilla and in 1945 were serving in the Far East. Although basically similar to the 'Q' class, they differed in one important respect which introduced a revolu-

Below:
The surviving 'Q' class destroyers were transferred to Australia and the Netherlands at the end of the war. Along with her sisters, HMAS *Quadrant* formed the 10th Destroyer Flotilla of the RAN. She is armed with four single 40mm Bofors to supplement the multiple 2pdr, but is otherwise unaltered and still retains a tripod foremast. *Real Photos (S2529)*

Above right:
HMAS *Queenborough*, seen at Portsmouth in 1958, was one of four Australian 'Q' class ships converted to Type 15 frigates. Layout differed slightly from the British ships and the twin 40mm mounting was positioned ahead of the raised bridge.
Wright and Logan

Right:
A sad sight as *Queenborough* is towed away for scrapping in 1975. *Maritime Photo Library*

Below right:
HMS *Rotherham*, seen in August 1946, still retains a lattice foremast with Type 291 radar at the masthead. A Type 271 lantern is over the searchlight platform together with the IFF aerials. *Wright and Logan*

Top:
Three 'R' class ships were sold to the Indian Navy in 1949. One of these was HMS *Redoubt*, shown here in her new guise as INS *Ranjit* in 1953. Changes include a new lattice foremast, updated radar equipment and the addition of single 40mm guns.
Maritime Photo Library

Above:
HMS *Rapid*, shown in 1946, was one of the ships refitted during the war with a lattice foremast and the standard destroyer radar outfit of Type 293 on the foremast and Type 291 on the mainmast aft.
Wright and Logan

Below:
HMS *Roebuck* at Glasgow in 1947. She is little altered from her wartime days. *Real Photos (S2933)*

tion into the internal accommodation arrangements. As a left-over from the days of sail, the ships' officers had traditionally been quartered in the after section of a warship while the rest of the crew accommodation was forward. In modern warships, this made little sense as most of the officers' duty stations were forward, on or near the bridge. However, traditions die hard in the Royal Navy and it took the experience of war to bring about a change which was introduced for the first time in a fleet destroyer aboard the 'R' class (although it had already been tried on the earlier 'Hunt' class escort destroyers).

During the war, many of the ships had their close range armament increased. For example, in 1945 *Raider* was equipped with a quadruple 2pdr, four single 40mm and two twin 20mm guns. She still retained a tripod foremast and carried a Type 271 surface warning radar amidships. Others, including *Racehorse*, *Redoubt* and *Rapid*, were refitted with a lattice foremast carrying a Type 291 Air Warning radar.

In early 1946 *Rotherham*, *Raider*, *Redoubt* and *Racehorse* went into reserve but in 1949 the first three completed a refit and were sold to the Indian Navy, being renamed *Rajput*, *Rana*, and *Rajit* respectively. All were fitted with lattice foremasts carrying Type 293 radar and retained a light AA armament consisting of the multiple 2pdr and six 20mm guns, except for *Rana* which had four 40mm instead of the 20mm guns. The other two were later altered to conform and all three had their torpedo tubes removed in 1962-63. They gave their new owners good service and were not scrapped until 1976.

HMS *Racehorse* was laid up at the end of the war and was subsequently used as a target ship and for trials to test the effects of various explosive charges against warship structures before being scrapped in 1949.

This left four ships (*Rapid*, *Relentless*, *Rocket* and *Roebuck*) and although *Relentless* spent the early postwar years mostly in reserve, the others saw active employment of varying periods up to 1950. At that time a series of studies concerning the future shape and role of the Royal Navy had identified a need for large numbers of fast AS frigates. The existing frigate fleet of wartime 'River', 'Loch' and 'Castle' classes was totally inadequate to deal with the threat posed by the new breed of fast underwater submarines (not, it should be noted, nuclear powered boats at this stage, but improved conventional types based on the wartime German Type XXI). The wartime frigates were too slow to engage a submarine effectively and too small to carry the new range of sonars and AS weapon systems which were becoming available. To meet this requirement, and to provide other new types of warship to meet the threat of air and sub-surface attack on convoys and task forces, a whole new range of frigate designs were prepared. These finally emerged as the Type 12 (anti-submarine), Type 14 (Utility AS), Type 41 (anti-aircraft) and Type 61 (Aircraft Direction) frigates which became the subject of an extensive construction programme throughout the 1950s and 1960s.

However, building new ships was expensive and the pace of the programme could not provide the overall numbers of escorts within the timescale set down by the Navy. At this time there was a very serious fear, based on various politico-military factors, that a large-scale war could break out around 1957 — particularly if the Western Alliance nations were seen to be in a weak position at that time. In order, therefore, to produce sufficient quantities of escort vessels in the time available, it was decided that the large number of destroyer hulls available in the postwar years should be converted to fast frigates. In 1947, it had already been decided that all remaining destroyers of the 'O' and 'P' classes and earlier would be rerated, and arrangements put in hand for their projected conversion. By 1949 the situation had changed in that many of the older ships had already been scrapped and, together with the fact that growing numbers of the destroyers laid down at the end of the war were now entering service, it was decided that the various emergency flotillas would also be converted. In fact, at that time, there were a total of 59 hulls available (from the 'M' through to the 'Z' classes) and it was intended that all should be converted in due course.

Mention has already been made (see 'M' class) of the proposed Type 62 conversion, but the most important conversions were the Types 15 and 16. In fact these were the only conversion programmes eventually implemented and it fell to two ships of the 'R' class (*Relentless* and *Rocket*) to act as the prototypes of the Type 15 conversion as described below. Details of the Type 16 conversion will be found in the section dealing with the 'T' class destroyers as these served as the prototypes in this case.

The two 'R' class ships were taken in hand in 1949 at Portsmouth and Devonport dockyards and began a two-year rebuilding which completely altered their appearance. All armament and superstructure was removed and the forecastle deck extended right aft, leaving only the original quarterdeck. A new bridge structure, extending the full width of the hull, was constructed and lattice masts erected fore and aft of the single raked funnel which had been retained. A new armament outfit included a twin Mk XIX 4in mounting aft, a Mk V twin 40mm Bofors forward above the bridge, and two Mk 10 Limbo AS mortars right aft. Originally the design also included AS torpedo tubes but the Mk 20E homing torpedo intended for use aboard these and other frigates was a total failure so that the torpedo tubes were subsequently removed from those ships which had them installed in the first place. The radar outfit included a Type 293Q at the top of the foremast, a Type 277Q height-finder/surface warning radar abaft the bridge, a Type 974 navigation radar and Type 262 gunnery radar on the MRS-1 Director.

As the major function of the ship was ASW, an improved sonar outfit was necessary and Types 170, 174 and 162 were installed. These provided the capability to search for and locate submarines and to provide precise information for the operation of the Limbo mortars. The original destroyer machinery was retained and standard displacement rose to around 2,300 tons resulting in a top speed of around 31kt.

The conversions of *Relentless* and *Rocket* were completed in 1951 and proved to be a great success. Consequently, the other two 'R' class ships (*Rapid* and *Roebuck*) were taken in hand the following year. Although it was originally intended that all 59 available destroyer hulls would undergo conversion to Type 15 frigates, the cost of such work (around £600,000 per ship) led to consideration of other less drastic schemes. By 1955 it was decided that future requirements would be met by new construction and no further conversions were

commenced after that date. The result of this was that only 23 Type 15s were completed for the Royal Navy although, as has already been mentioned, four of the Australian 'Q' class were similarly converted. These were almost identical to the British version except that the navigation bridge was one deck higher and further aft so that the twin 40mm was mounted forward of the bridge structure. As will be seen, two similar conversions were also carried out by the Canadian Navy on two ships of later classes.

Since this book is primarily concerned with the development of the destroyer, the subsequent career of ships converted to frigates will not be covered. However, the reader is referred to the author's previous book in this series (*Royal Navy Frigates 1945-1983*, published by Ian Allan in 1983) for fuller details of these and other frigates. At this point it is sufficient to note all four 'R' class Type 15s remained in service for a lengthy period until the late 1960s and *Rapid* survived until 1981 when she was expended as a target ship.

Name	No	Laid Down	Launched	Completed	Builder	Yard	Remarks	
Quadrant	D11	24/09/40	28/02/42	26/11/42	Hawthorn Leslie	Hebburn	RAN 1945. Type 15. Sold off	07/01/63
Quality	G62	10/10/40	06/10/41	07/09/42	Swan Hunter	Tyne	RAN. Sold, B/Up Tokyo Japan	10/04/58
Queenborough	D270	06/11/40	16/01/42	10/12/42	Swan Hunter	Tyne	RAN 1945. Type 15. Scrapped Japan	1975
Quiberon	D281	14/10/40	31/01/42	22/07/42	J. S. White	Cowes	RAN 1942. Type 15. Scrapped Japan	1972
Quickmatch	D292	06/02/41	11/04/42	30/09/42	J. S. White	Cowes	RAN 1945. Type 15. B/Up Osaka	1972
Quilliam	G09	19/08/40	29/11/41	22/10/42	Hawthorn Leslie	Hebburn	RNethN. B/Up Burght, Holland	08/02/57
Racehorse	H11	25/06/41	01/06/42	30/10/42	J. Brown	Clydebank	Arr Troon for scrap	08/12/49
Raider	D115	16/04/41	01/04/42	16/11/42	Cammell Laird	Birkenhead	IN 1949. Scrapped	1976
Rapid	D138	16/06/41	16/07/42	20/02/43	Cammell Laird	Birkenhead	Type 15. Expended as target	12/81
Rotherham	D209	10/04/41	21/03/42	27/08/42	J. Brown	Clydebank	IN 1949. Scrapped	1976
Redoubt	D141	19/06/41	02/05/42	01/10/42	J. Brown	Clydebank	IN 1949. Scrapped	1976
Relentless	H85	20/06/41	15/07/42	30/11/42	J. Brown	Clydebank	Type 15. Scrapped Inverkeithing	1971
Rocket	H92	14/03/41	28/10/42	04/08/43	Scotts	Greenock	Type 15. Arr Dalmuir for scrap	03/67
Roebuck	D195	19/06/41	10/12/42	10/06/43	Scotts	Greenock	Type 15. Inverkeithing for scrap	08/08/68

Data: 'R' class, HMS *Raider* (1945)
Displacement (tons): 1,705 standard, 2,425 full load
Length/Beam (ft): 358 (oa)/35.75
Draught (ft): 9.5 (light), 13.5 (full load)
Armament: 4×4.7in, 1×quadruple 2pdr AA, 4×single 40mm, 2×twin 20mm guns, 8×21in torpedo tubes, depth charges
Radars: Types 291, 271, 285
Machinery: 2×Admiralty 3-drum boilers (300lb/sq in/630°F), 2×shafts, Parsons geared turbines, 40,000shp
Speed/Range: 32kt/4,675nm @ 20kt
Oil Fuel (tons): 615
Complement: c200

Data: Type 15 frigate, HMS *Rocket* (1955)
Displacement (tons): 2,300 standard, 2,700 full load
Length/Beam (ft): 358 (oa)/35.75
Draught (ft): 14.5 (full load)
Armament: 2×4in on 1×twin Mk XIX mounting, 2×40mm on Mk V Utility twin mounting, 2×Mk 10 Limbo A/S mortars
Radars: Types 293Q, 277Q, 974, 262
Machinery: As destroyer
Speed/Range: 31kt/2,800nm @ 20kt
Oil Fuel (tons): 580
Complement: 174

'S' Class Destroyers — *Savage, Saumerez, Scorpion, Scourge, Serapis, Success*

With the 'S' class, the development of a standard design for the wartime Emergency Flotillas reached a stage which was substantially unaltered for subsequent classes. Basically, they employed the same hull, machinery and layout of the preceding 'R' class (which in turn utilised the 'J' class hull and machinery) but introduced a number of improvements brought about by war experience and the availability (at last) of better weapon systems.

One noticeable difference was a modified bow which had a greater rake than the 'J' and 'R' class designs and this increased overall length by 4ft 6in, reducing spray over the forecastle and bridge. However, the major improvement was in the armament which consisted of four single 4.7in guns in new pattern mountings (designated CP Mk XXII) which increased elevation to 55°. These featured a new gunshield design with a sloping face which readily identified the new mounting. Rate of fire was also increased as the new mounting had a spring operated rammer which was set by the recoil action, replacing the previous hand operated system.

The light AA armament was improved with the deletion of the long-enduring 2pdr mounting which was replaced by the radar directed Mk IV (Hazemeyer) twin 40mm mounting. This had been developed from a fully stabilised 40mm AA mounting originally designed by the Dutch Navy, details of which became available to the RN in 1940. In order to improve arcs of fire, the twin 40mm was mounted on what was previously the searchlight platform between the torpedo tubes and the remainder of the light AA armament was made up of four twin 20mm in the bridge wings and abaft the funnel.

As usual, supply shortages meant that one ship (*Scorpion*) was completed with a multiple 2pdr instead of the twin 40mm, while *Swift* and *Savage* originally carried two extra twin 20mm instead. Another variation was that the last four ships were completed with a lattice foremast to carry the increasing load of electronic equipment which was becoming standard on warships. Normal radar outfit in these ships was Type 271 surface warning on the lattice foremast and Type 291 air warning on a pole mast aft, while the usual Type 285 was on the director and the Hazemeyer mounting had the short range Type 282.

One ship, HMS *Savage*, introduced yet another variation which was of particular significance. While the new main armament of the 'S' class could now elevate to 55°, this still did not constitute a true high-angle (HA) mounting (such as the US Navy had enjoyed throughout the war). In fact, a true HA installation (Mk XII) had been developed before the war for the 4.7in gun and was fitted to the battleships *Rodney* and *Nelson*, but this had always been regarded as too large and heavy for destroyer use. However, a twin HA mounting based on the 4.5in gun had been produced before the war for installation aboard aircraft carriers and some of the modernised battleships and battlecruisers. This was developed into the Mk IV twin 4.5in mounting, with an elevation of 80°, which was to become the standard armament of the 'Battle' class destroyers (described in Chapter 4). However, the first destroyer to carry the new turret was HMS *Savage*, forward of the bridge and replacing the two single guns in A and B positions. To ensure uniformity, X and Y mountings were also 4.5in guns but carried in the standard CP XXII and still restricted to 55° elevation. There was little difference in the performance of the 4.7in and 4.5in and the latter actually fired a 55lb shell compared with the 50lb shell of the nominally larger gun.

All eight ships entered service in late 1943 and joined the Home Fleet as the 23rd Destroyer Flotilla. Two (*Shark* and *Swift*) were war losses, the former having previously been transferred to the Norwegian Navy and renamed *Svenner*. *Saumerez* was later transferred to the Far East and, as leader of the 26th Flotilla, took part in the famous night action of 16 May 1945, when a force of British destroyers sank the Japanese cruiser *Haguro* in a classic torpedo action. After the war she returned home but in 1946 was part of the Mediterranean Fleet. Here she was heavily damaged on 22 October 1946 when she hit an Albanian-laid mine in the notorious Corfu Channel Incident. Although salvaged and eventually towed home, she was not repaired and was finally scrapped in 1950.

The odd man out, *Savage*, was more fortunate and, having survived the war, continued in service for many years. The twin 4.5in turret was ideal for training purposes and she served in this role until 1947 when she was laid up. Subsequently, she was used as a trials ship for experiments with new propeller designs intended for use on the new generation of frigates. For this purpose the stern structure was modified so that glass underwater viewing ports were provided to allow the scientists to observe the action of the propellers. On completion of these trials in 1952 *Savage* was refitted but spent much of her subsequent career in reserve, being scrapped in 1962.

Saumerez and *Savage* were the only ships of the class to see postwar service with the Royal Navy as the remaining ships were all transferred to foreign navies. *Success* was transferred to the Norwegian Navy and renamed *Stord* on completion, and was retained by them after 1945. Later renumbered D300 (original pendant number G26) she remained in service for many years before being scrapped in 1959.

The remaining three ships (*Scorpion*, *Scourge* and *Serapis*) were transferred in 1945 to the Royal Netherlands Navy and renamed *Kortenaer*, *Evertsen* and *Piet Hein* respectively. Much of their subsequent career was in the Far East, first in the waters around the Netherlands East Indies until 1948 and later in support of United Nations operations in the Korean War. During this period they were substantially unaltered but between 1956 and 1958 all three were redesigned as frigates and rebuilt with a helicopter operating deck amidships. Their remaining life was relatively short although *Kortenaer* and *Evertsen* were again in the Far East at the start of the Indonesian Confrontation, on one occasion (in January 1962) sinking three Indonesian fast patrol boats which attacked them. However, all three ships had been decommissioned by the end of the year and were scrapped almost immediately.

Name	No	Laid Down	Launched	Completed	Builder	Yard	Remarks	
Savage	D27	07/12/41	24/09/42	08/06/43	Hawthorn Leslie	Hebburn	Arr Newport for scrap	11/04/62
Saumerez	G12	09/41	20/11/42	07/43	Hawthorn Leslie	Hebburn	Arr Charlestown for scrap	08/09/50
Scorpion	G72	19/06/41	26/08/42	11/05/43	Cammell Laird	Birkenhead	RNethN. Arr Ghent for scrap	18/07/63
Scourge	GOL	26/06/41	08/12/42	14/07/43	Cammell Laird	Birkenhead	RNethN. Scrapped Holland	00/07/63
Separis	G94	14/08/41	25/03/43	23/12/43	Scotts	Greenock	RNethN. Arr Ghent for scrap	30/05/62
Success	G26	25/02/42	03/04/43	06/09/43	J. S. White	Cowes	RNN. Scrapped Burght, Belgium	1959

Data: 'S' class, HMS *Saumerez* (1946)
Displacement (tons): 1,710 standard, 2,530 full load
Length/Beam (ft): 363.5 (oa)/35.75
Draught (ft): 10 (light), 14.5 (full load)
Armament: 4×4.7in on single CP Mk XXII mountings, 1×Mk IV Hazemeyer twin 40mm mounting, 4×single 40mm guns, 8×21in torpedo tubes, depth charges
Radars: Types 293, 291, 285, 282
Machinery: As 'R' class
Speed/Range: 32kt/4,675nm @ 20kt
Oil Fuel (tons): 615
Complement: 225

'T' Class Destroyers — *Teazer, Tenacious, Termagent, Terpsichore, Troubridge, Tumult, Tuscan, Tyrian*

These eight ships formed the 6th Flotilla of the Emergency War Programme and were generally identical to the preceding flotilla. Laid down in 1941, some of them actually entered service before some of the 'S' class due to the pace of the destroyer building programme. The first four ships (*Troubridge, Tumult, Tuscan, Tyrian*) were all completed with tripod foremasts, but the rest had the more modern lattice mast. Short range AA armament varied according to availability but a typical example was *Teazer* which was completed with twin 40mm amidships and eight 20mm in a mix of twin and single mounts. A full torpedo armament (two quadruple mountings) was carried, while radar outfit consisted of Types 291, 272 or 271, and 285 while most were also fitted with HF/DF.

During the course of the war, the AA armament was progressively improved by the substitution of 40mm guns for the earlier 20mm and Type 293 radar replaced the earlier 271 or 272 originally fitted. Thus, by the end of the war, *Tumult* carried two single 40mm in the bridge wings, three single 40mm on a platform abaft and funnel and a twin 40mm Hazemeyer mounting between the torpedo tubes. A lattice foremast carried Type 293 surface warning radar and HF/DF, while Type 291 air warning was carried on a polemast aft.

None of the class was lost during the war and they quickly paid off into reserve. However, *Troubridge* was hastily reactivated in 1946 to replace *Saumerez* after that ship had been mined in the Corfu Channel, acting as leader of the 3rd Destroyer Flotilla in the Mediterranean until 1949.

Mention has already been made of the extensive programme set in hand in 1949 to convert the remaining destroyers to fast AS frigates, but the Type 15 full conversion was an expensive and time consuming project (typically £600,000 and over 18 months work per ship) and the Naval Staff therefore looked at various conversion schemes which could produce the required capability at reduced cost. Initially, none of the reduced designs appeared to offer an acceptable solution but, as always, lack of money forced a reconsideration

Below:
HMS *Tumult* enters Portsmouth to pay off into reserve in March 1946. She carries a Hazemeyer twin 40mm mounting between the torpedo tubes and three single 40mm abaft the funnel.
Wright and Logan

Right:
As a consequence of the damage to HMS *Saumerez*, *Troubridge* was taken out of reserve and replaced her as leader of the 3rd Destroyer Squadron in the Mediterranean. Note the leader's black band around the top of the funnel.

Below right:
With the exception of *Troubridge*, all the 'T' class destroyers were converted to Type 16 frigates. The prototype was HMS *Tenacious* which is shown at the 1953 Coronation Review. She carries a twin 4in gun forward, a hefty light AA armament of no less than seven 40mm guns, a set of torpedo tubes and two Squid mortars on the after deckhouse. In the background is the Canadian 'River' class frigate *La Hulloise*. *Skyfotos*

and in 1949 HMS *Tenacious* was earmarked as a prototype for the Type 16 limited conversion programme.

Compared to the Type 15, the Type 16 retained the basic destroyer hull and superstructure and alterations were confined to the armament and sensor outfit. As converted, *Tenacious* carried a twin 4in Mk XIX AA mounting in B position (all 4.7in guns having been removed), seven 40mm guns (one twin and five single), and two Squid AS mortars on the roof of the after deckhouse. One set of torpedo tubes was retained and were intended to fire AS torpedoes, although an effective weapon was never available. Radar comprised a Type 293Q and 974 navigation radar on the lattice foremast, together with HF/DF. Sonars included Type 146B (later 147F), Type 162, and Type 174. A Type 16 conversion was

estimated to cost £260,000 — less than half the price of a Type 15 — and the work would take less than 12 months.

Following *Tenacious*, which was converted in 1951-52, the other ships of the class, except *Troubridge*, were also rebuilt as Type 16s between 1952 and 1954. *Teazer*, *Tumult* and *Terpsichore* differed from the others in that they were fitted with a new, fully enclosed bridge with an operations room below. As mentioned earlier, the Type 16 conversion was also carried out to various 'O' and 'P' class destroyers which also acted as fast minelayers, so that a total of 10 such conversions were carried out for the Royal Navy.

Troubridge was the exception to the above and was actually given the full Type 15 conversion — the initial work being carried out by Portsmouth Dockyard — but later the ship was towed to J. S.

White's yard at Cowes for completion. She differed from earlier Type 15s by having a different bridge structure carried a deck higher and the twin 40mm guns were moved forward — a layout similar to the 'Q' class as converted in Australia.

The Type 16 was not a particularly sophisticated ship compared with the full conversions of the 'R' and other classes and consequently they were phased out of service as frigates from the new construction programmes were completed. In particular, the Squid mortar was really obsolete and at one point there were plans to replace them with a single Mk 10 Limbo, but this was never implemented. *Troubridge* was the last survivor, having an active career until finally paying off at Chatham in 1969.

The limitations of the Type 16 led to serious consideration of an alternative project which was designated Type 18. This was a sort of 'half-way house' between the other conversions and was put forward in 1950. In this case the basic destroyer hull was retained and the forecastle deck not extended aft. Gun armament would be the same as the Type 15 (ie two 4in and two 40mm), but one

Above:
HMS *Troubridge* was the only 'T' class converted to a Type 15 frigate. She was one of three conversions to feature a new enclosed bridge with the twin 40mm guns positioned in front. In other respects she was almost identical to the 'R' class Type 15s.
Wright and Logan

set of torpedo tubes would be retained and two Limbo mortars carried aft at weather deck level, necessitating a protective breakwater. Sonars of Types 170/174/162 would be carried, and together with the radar outfit similar to the Type 15 except that there would be no room for the Type 277Q. This design was costed at £450,000 and would take 15 months per ship. At one point it was proposed that the Type 18 should replace both the other types in the conversion programme as it offered considerable cost savings without sacrificing too much operational capability. The five surviving 'N' class were earmarked as the initial group to be converted, although funding would not be available until 1954-55. By that time it had been decided that resources would be concentrated on new construction and so the project died.

Name	No	Laid Down	Launched	Completed	Builder	Yard	Remarks	
Teazer	D23	20/10/41	07/01/43	13/09/43	Cammell Laird	Birkenhead	Type 16. Arr Dalmuir for scrap	07/08/65
Troubridge	D40	10/11/41	23/09/42	08/03/43	J. Brown	Clydebank	Type 15. B/Up J. Cashmore, Newport	1970
Tenacious	D45	03/12/41	24/03/43	30/10/43	Cammell Laird	Birkenhead	Type 16. Arr Troon for scrap	29/06/65
Termagent	D189	25/11/41	22/03/43	18/10/43	Denny	Dunbarton	Type 16. Arr Dalmuir for scrap	05/11/65
Terpsichore	D33	25/11/41	17/06/43	20/01/44	Denny	Dunbarton	Type 16. Arr Troon for scrap	17/05/66
Tumult	D121	16/11/41	09/11/42	02/04/43	J. Brown	Clydebank	Type 16. Arr Dalmuir for scrap	25/10/65
Tuscan	D156	09/09/41	28/05/42	08/04/43	Swan Hunter	Tyne	Type 16. Arr Bo'ness for scrap	26/05/66
Tyrian	D67	15/10/41	27/07/42	08/04/43	Swan Hunter	Tyne	Type 16. Arr Troon for scrap	09/03/65

Data: 'T' class, HMS *Tumult* (1946)
Displacement (tons): 1,802 standard, 2,530 full load
Length/Beam (ft): 363 (oa)/35.75
Draught (ft): 10 (light), 14.5 (full load)
Armament: 4×4.7in on 4×single mountings, 1×Hazemeyer Mk IV twin 40mm mounting, 5×single 40mm, 8×21in torpedo tubes, depth charges
Radars: Types 293, 291, 285
Machinery: As 'R' class
Speed/Range: 32kt/4,675nm @ 20kt
Oil Fuel (tons): 615
Complement: 180

Data: Type 16 frigate, HMS *Teazer* (1955)
Displacement (tons): 1,800 standard, 2,300 full load
Length/Beam (ft): 363 (oa)/35.75
Draught (ft): 14.5 (full load)
Armament: 2×4in on 1×Mk XIX twin mounting, 1×Mk V twin 40mm mounting, 5×single 40mm, 8×21in torpedo tubes, 2×Squid AS mortars
Radars: Types 293Q, 291, 974
Machinery: As 'R' class destroyer
Speed/Range: As built
Oil Fuel (tons): As built
Complement: 175

'U', 'V' and 'W' Class Destroyers — *Grenville, Ulster, Ulysses, Undaunted, Undine, Urania, Urchin, Ursa, Valentine, Venus, Verulam, Vigilant, Virago, Vixen, Volage, Kempenfelt, Wager, Wakeful, Wessex, Whelp, Whirlwind, Wizard, Wrangler*

By 1942, the Emergency Programme was in full swing and these 24 ships were all laid down in late 1941 and 1942, entering service in 1943-44. All except *Grenville*, *Ulster* and *Venus* were completed with lattice foremasts and were, again, repeats of the 'S' class design. AA armament varied with many of the later ships being equipped with 40mm and 2pdr guns to combat Kamikaze attacks in the Pacific.

These ships comprised the 7th, 8th and 9th Emergency Flotillas and while the alphabetical system of naming was adhered to, it is interesting to note that the flotilla leaders were given names out of sequence which perpetuated the names of flotilla leaders from other classes which had already been lost in the war. Out of the three flotillas, only *Hardy*, the 'V' class leader, was lost although *Ulster* was seriously damaged by a Kamikaze off Okinawa in April 1945. By mid-1945, all the remainder were serving with the British Pacific Fleet or Far East Fleet — *Verulam*, *Vigilant*, *Venus* and *Virago* being involved in the sinking of the Japanese cruiser *Haguro*.

Grenville and the rest of the 'U' class returned home at the end of the war and spent the next few years in reserve. One exception was *Ulster* which, following her war damage, was extensively repaired and refitted between 1945 and February 1946. She then recommissioned and acted as a training ship based at Rosyth until 1949. All eight underwent reconstruction as Type 15 full conver-

Below:
A wartime shot of HMS *Undine* as completed in December 1943. Note the lattice mast and the Hazemeyer twin 40mm mounting amidships.
Vosper Thornycroft

sion frigates between 1952 and 1956, several subsequently serving well into the 1970s as trials and training ships after being withdrawn from front line service. Last of the class was *Grenville* which was finally scrapped in 1983.

Of the 'V' class, *Hardy* was sunk and *Valentine* and *Vixen* were transferred to the RCN on completion, being renamed *Algonquin* and *Sioux*. After returning from the Far East at the end of the war, the five Royal Navy ships served as the 3rd Destroyer Flotilla in the Mediterranean until 1949 when they paid off into reserve. During this period *Volage* was also damaged in the Corfu Incident, losing most of her bow, but was towed to Malta where she was eventually repaired. As with many other remaining destroyers, they were converted to Type 15 full conversion frigates between 1951 and 1955 although they were fitted with Squid AS mortars instead of the Limbo in other ships. They also followed the pattern of several years' service with the various frigate squadrons, followed by periods as training and trials ships before being scrapped — *Vigilant* and *Virago* in 1965 and the others in 1972.

The two Canadian ships were also converted to frigates. *Algonquin* was given the full Type 15 treatment at Esquimault Dockyard in 1954 but had a different bridge structure to the British ships and carried a US pattern twin 3in mounting forward as well as the twin 4in aft. US radars were carried on the lattice foremast and, later, a funnel cowl was fitted which gave the ship a very different appearance from her British sister ships. She was scrapped at Taiwan in 1971.

The other former 'V' class ship, HMCS *Sioux* was also converted to an AS frigate but along lines even more limited than the Royal Navy's Type 16.

she retained her two forward 4.7in guns and one set of torpedo tubes, but all other armament was removed and an extended deckhouse aft carried two Squid mortars. Light AA armament comprised one twin and four single 40mm guns. A funnel cowl was also fitted. She decommissioned in 1963 and was scrapped in 1965.

Finally we come to the eight 'W' class which, like the others, also ended the war in the Far East and subsequently returned home. Four ships (*Kempenfelt*, *Wager*, *Wessex* and *Whelp*) paid off into reserve but, in 1948, transferred to the South African dockyard at Simonstown where they were again laid up. The other four remained active with the Plymouth and Portsmouth local flotillas until being taken in hand for Type 15 conversion in 1951-53. Of these, *Wakeful* was the last active example in RN service, finishing her days as a tender and trials ship for the ASWE at Portsmouth.

However, she was outlived by *Wrangler* which was sold to South Africa in 1957 and renamed *Vrystaat*. Here she joined two of her sister ships, *Wessex* and *Whelp*, which had previously been transferred to the SAN in 1950 and 1953 respectively, their new names being *Jan van Riebeeck* and *Simon van der Stel*. Originally employed as traditional destroyers, the two ships were modernised between 1962 and 1964 as AS frigates along the lines of the Type 16 conversion. However, as with other Commonwealth navies, there were differences in layout and armament. In this case the ships were rearmed with two twin 4in mountings in B and Y positions and four single 40mm, while one set of torpedo tubes was retained. However, an innovation for this type of conversion was the construction of a hangar and

Left:
HMS *Urania* in the Mediterranean after the end of the war. She carries three single 40mm guns abaft the funnel, and a further pair in the bridge wings.
Real Photos (1681)

Centre left:
HMS *Grenville*, originally built as the 'U' class flotilla leader, was converted to a Type 15 frigate in 1953-54. This aerial view clearly shows the layout of these frigates with the rounded bridge surmounted by the twin 40mm mounting forward, and the twin 4in and Limbo mortars aft. *Real Photos (9936)*

Bottom left:
A close-up of the bridge of HMS *Virago* in 1948. Of particular interest are the pedestal mounted Mk II(W) rangefinder director carrying a Type 285 radar and the destroyer DCT, both at the after end of the bridge. This arrangement was standard on Emergency Programme destroyers from the 'Q' to 'V' classes inclusive. *Maritime Photo Library*

Below:
Volage was also seriously damaged in the Corfu Incident (qv *Saumerez*), losing her bows. However she did not lose power and was able to tow *Saumerez* out of the minefield by going astern — an excellent piece of seamanship by her Captain, Cdr R. Paul RN. *Imperial War Museum*

helicopter landing pad over the after superstructure. Two Westland Wasp helicopters could be carried and at a later date the 21in torpedo tubes were removed and replaced by two triple 12.75in ASW torpedo tubes abreast the hangar. The old Type 293 radar was retained at the masthead, although a modern X-band fire control radar replaced the former bridge-mounted DCT.

Vrystaat (ex-*Wrangler*) was expended as a target ship in 1976 while the *Simon van der Stel* was scrapped in 1976 and *Jan van Riebeeck* was sunk as a target in 1980.

The two remaining 'W' class in reserve at Simonstown in the early 1950s were *Kempenfelt* and *Wager* which were sold to Yugoslavia in 1956 after it had been established that they would not be required by the Royal Navy for conversion to frigates. They were towed to that country for refitting but were not substantially altered, retaining the 4.7in guns and 21in torpedo tubes. They did not recommission until the end of 1959 and were scrapped in 1971.

Above:
Transferred to the RCN on completion, HMS *Vixen* was renamed *Sioux* and remained in service until 1963. Although redesignated as a frigate, she retained much of her destroyer armament, losing just the after guns and torpedo tubes to make way for an extended deckhouse carrying two Squid mortars. *Real Photos (S2122)*

Data:	'U' class, HMS *Ulysses* (1951)
Displacement (tons):	1,777 standard, 2,508 full load
Length/Beam (ft):	363 (oa)/35.75
Draught (ft):	10 (light), 14.5 (full load)
Armament:	4×single 4.7in, 5×single 40mm AA, 8×21in torpedo tubes, depth charges
Radars:	Types 293, 291 285
Machinery:	As 'R' class
Speed/Range:	32kt
Oil Fuel (tons):	615
Complement:	179

Name	No	Laid Down	Launched	Completed	Builder	Yard	Remarks	
Grenville	D197	01/11/41	12/10/42	27/05/43	Swan Hunter	Tyne	Type 15. Scrapped	1983
Ulster	D83	12/11/41	09/11/42	30/06/43	Swan Hunter	Tyne	Type 15. Scrapped Inverkeithing	1980
Ulysses	D169	14/03/42	22/04/43	23/12/43	Cammell Laird	Birkenhead	Type 15. Scrapped Plymouth	1970
Undaunted	D53	08/09/42	19/07/43	03/03/44	Cammell Laird	Birkenhead	Type 15. Sunk as target	1978
Undine	D142	10/03/42	01/06/43	23/12/43	Thornycroft	Woolston	Type 15. Arr Newport for scrap	14/11/65
Urania	D105	18/06/42	19/05/43	18/01/44	Vickers Armstrong	Barrow	Type 15. Scrapped Faslane	1971
Urchin	D199	22/03/42	08/03/43	24/09/43	Vickers Armstrong	Barrow	Type 15. Arr Troon for scrap	06/08/67
Ursa	D222	02/05/42	22/07/43	01/03/44	Thornycroft	Woolston	Type 15. Arr Newport for scrap	09/67
Valentine	224	08/10/42	02/09/43	28/02/44	J. Brown	Clydebank	RCN 1944. Scrapped	1971
Venus	D50	12/01/42	23/02/43	28/08/43	Fairfield	Govan	Type 15. Scrapped Briton Ferry	1972
Verulam	D28	26/01/42	22/04/43	10/12/43	Fairfield	Govan	Type 15. B/Up J. Cashmore, Newport	1972
Vigilant	D93	31/01/42	22/12/42	10/09/43	Swan Hunter	Tyne	Type 15. Arr Faslane for scrap	04/06/65
Virago	D75	16/02/42	04/02/43	05/11/43	Swan Hunter	Tyne	Type 15. Arr Faslane for scrap	04/06/65
Vixen	225	31/10/42	14/09/43	05/03/44	J. S. White	Cowes	RCN. Arr La Spezia for scrap	20/08/65
Volage	D41	31/12/42	15/12/43	26/05/44	J. S. White	Cowes	Type 15. B/Up Portsmouth Shipbreakers	1972
Kempenfelt	D103	24/06/42	08/05/43	25/10/43	J. Brown	Clydebank	Yugoslav Navy 1958. B/Up Split.	1970
Wager	D298	20/11/42	01/11/43	14/04/44	J. Brown	Clydebank	Yugoslav Navy 1958. B/Up Split	1971
Wakeful	D159	03/06/42	30/06/43	17/02/44	Fairfield	Govan	Type 15. Scrapped Inverkeithing	1971
Wessex	D78	20/10/42	03/09/43	09/05/44	Fairfield	Govan	SAN 1950. Sunk as target	1980
Whelp	D237	01/05/42	03/06/43	26/04/44	Hawthorn Leslie	Hebburn	SAN 1953. Scrapped	1976
Whirlwind	D187	31/07/42	30/08/43	20/07/44	Hawthorn Leslie	Hebburn	Type 15. Expended as target	10/74
Wizard	D72	14/09/42	29/09/43	30/03/44	Vickers Armstrong	Barrow	Type 15. Inverkiething for scrap	07/03/67
Wrangler	D158	23/09/42	30/12/43	14/07/44	Vickers Armstrong	Barrow	SAN 1957. Type 15. Sunk as target	04/76

Above:
An excellent shot of HMS *Wizard* in the early 1950s before conversion to a Type 15 frigate. Note the new rangefinder director Mk III(W) which replaced the Mk II(W) and destroyer DCT carried by the previous classes. She carries a rather mixed light AA outfit consisting of twin Hazemeyer 40mm mounting between the torpedo tubes, two single 40mm guns abaft the funnel, and single 2pdrs in the bridge wings. *Skyfotos*

Below:
HMS *Whelp* was sold to South Africa in 1953 and was converted to a frigate in 1962-64. In her new guise she was similar to the British Type 16 frigates but carried an extra twin 4in mounting right aft and was also fitted with a hangar and flight deck for two Wasp helicopters. *Maritime Photo Library*

'Z' Class Destroyers — *Myngs, Zephyr, Zambesi, Zealous, Zebra, Zenith, Zest, Zodiac*

This was the 10th Flotilla of the Emergency War Programme and they differed from the preceding classes in only one important respect. The 4.7in gun, which has been the standard destroyer armament since the end of World War 1, was replaced by the new 4.5in Mk IV gun in Mk V mountings, the latter being an adaptation of the CP XXII mounting used in Classes 'S' to 'W'. Maximum elevation remained at 55° and a new combined HA/LA director (Mk I Type K) replaced the separate installations which equipped earlier classes. This was basically an interim system with many faults, but the more advanced Mk VI director was in short supply and was reserved for use on the first of the new 'Battle' class destroyers which were then building.

Apart from the main armament, these ships were otherwise identical to the previous Emergency Flotillas and were completed with lattice foremasts carrying Type 293 radar with Type 291 on a polemast stepped aft. *Myngs* and *Zephyr* were fitted as flotilla leaders.

The 'Z' class were laid down in 1942 but completion was delayed because of shortages of the new guns and directors and they did not enter service until late 1944. Being equipped, like the 'S' class, for Arctic use, they served initially with the Home Fleet on Russian Convoy duties.

In the immediate postwar period *Myngs, Zephyr, Zest, Zambesi, Zebra* and *Zenith* formed the 4th Destroyer Flotilla with the Home Fleet while the remaining two ships served with the 2nd Flotilla. All were laid up in reserve in 1947 but *Zest* was reactivated later in the year and saw further service until 1954 when she was taken in hand at Chatham for conversion to a Type 15 frigate. It had been intended that all eight ships would be rebuilt but plans for the rest were cancelled in 1955. Subsequently *Zephyr, Zambesi* and *Zebra* were scrapped in 1958-59.

However, the decision not to convert these ships meant that they were available for sale to foreign navies and in 1955 the remaining four were all sold. *Myngs* and *Zenith* went to the Egyptian Navy to become *El Qaher* and *El Fateh* respectively. Both ships were refitted before transfer in 1956 but remained substantially unaltered from their immediate postwar appearance. Delivery to their new owners in August 1956 caused a furore at home as the government had announced an embargo on the export of arms to Egypt following Colonel Nasser's seizure of the Suez Canal earlier in the year. Eventually they were permitted to sail, but without ammunition or torpedoes.

In 1963 they returned to the UK for a further refit at J. S. White's Cowes yard when the torpedo tubes were landed, a new Mk VI HA/LA director was installed, and a Type 960 long-range radar fitted on a new lattice mast stepped aft. In this form they returned to service with the Egyptian Navy but *El Qaher* was sunk by Israeli aircraft in 1970. The other ship, *El Fateh* was renumbered 833 and would appear to be still in existence, although laid up.

To make sure that the UK should be seen to be even handed in its approach to Middle East politics, the remaining two ships (*Zealous* and *Zodiac*) were sold to Israel, also in 1955; their new names being *Eilat* and *Yaffa*. They were also refitted before transfer but, again, were substantially unaltered and retained the torpedo tubes. Light AA armament was rationalised to six 40mm

Above:
HMS *Zest* had an active career in the postwar years until she was laid up in 1952 pending her conversion into a frigate. This view shows her in that year with Y gun and all light AA armament (except the Hazemeyer) removed. *Real Photos (6224)*

Below:
A rather sorry looking HMS *Zenith* off Spithead in 1953. Part of the reserve fleet, her guns and other equipment are cocooned to protect them from the ravages of the elements. *Skyfotos*

guns. *Eilat* was to gain a notorious spot in naval history by becoming the first victim of a guided missile launched from another surface vessel when she was sunk by Styx missiles from an Egyptian FPB off Alexandria in October 1967. This event sent shock waves of concern through the world's major navies as it demonstrated how vulnerable were major warships to this type of attack. The other ship, *Yaffa*, remained in service until it was laid up in 1972 and subsequently scrapped. Since that time the Israeli Navy, as a result of their experience, has only operated small combat ships such as fast patrol boats and missile-armed corvettes.

Despite reaching the end of the alphabet, production of the Emergency War Flotilla ships, to the same basic design, continued. However, as the postwar career of subsequent ships was markedly different to those we have reviewed up to now, it is appropriate to deal with them in a new chapter.

Above:
Only one 'Z' class destroyer, HMS *Zest*, was converted to a Type 15 frigate and the others were sold off or scrapped in the mid-1950s. This view of *Zest* as converted shows the layout of the two Mk 10 Limbo mortars on the quarterdeck. *Royal Navy*

Data:	'Z' class leader, HMS *Myngs* (1950)
Displacement (tons):	1,710 standard, 2,530 full load
Length/Beam (ft):	363 (oa)/35.75
Draught (ft):	10 (light), 14.5 (full load)
Armament:	4×single 4.5in Mk IV on CP Mk V mountings, 1×Hazemeyer Mk IV twin 40mm mounting, 4×single 40mm, 8×21in torpedo tubes, depth charges
Radars:	Types 293, 291, 285, 282
Machinery:	As 'R' class
Speed/Range:	32kt/4,675nm @ 20kt
Oil Fuel (tons):	615
Complement:	222

Name	No	Laid Down	Launched	Completed	Builder	Yard	Remarks	
Myngs	D06	27/05/42	31/05/43	23/06/44	Vickers Armstrong	Tyne	To Egypt 1955. Sunk Israeli A/C	16/05/70
Zambesi	D66	21/12/42	21/11/43	18/07/44	Cammell Laird	Birkenhead	Arr Briton Ferry for scrap	12/12/59
Zealous	D39	05/05/43	28/02/44	09/10/44	Cammell Laird	Birkenhead	ISR N 1955. Sunk by missile	21/10/67
Zebra	D81	14/05/42	08/03/44	13/10/44	Denny	Dunbarton	Arr Newport for scrap	12/02/59
Zenith	D95	19/05/42	05/06/44	22/12/44	Denny	Dunbarton	EGYPT N 1955. In service	01/01/87
Zephyr	D19	13/07/42	15/07/43	06/09/44	Vickers Armstrong	Tyne	Arr Dunston for scrap	02/07/58
Zest	D02	21/07/42	14/10/43	20/07/44	Thornycroft	Woolston	Type 15. Scrapped Dalmuir	1970
Zodiac	D54	07/11/42	11/03/44	23/10/44	Thornycroft	Woolston	ISR N 1955. Laid up	1972

3 The 'C' Group Destroyers

is a measure of the pace of the wartime building ogramme that orders for a further Emergency otilla (11th) were placed only four days after the der had been placed for the preceding 'Z' class. is was in February 1942 and the new ships, tended to be exact repeats of the previous class, re laid down in late 1942 and early 1943. In fact aval Staff Requirements now called for all new stroyers to be fitted with the new Mk VI HA/LA rector together with remote power control for e guns. However, it was recognised in 1942 that oduction of this equipment would not be fficient to meet demand until 1945 at the earliest d so it was accepted that the interim arrange- ent introduced with the 'Z' class should be ntinued.

The naming of the new ships presented a oblem. The obvious solution of reverting back to e beginning of the alphabet had the drawback at ships of the earlier flotillas were still in istence and therefore there was the risk of nfusion and possible misidentification. Initially it as decided to revive a variety of traditional stroyer names from the flotillas built in the latter lf of World War 1. These were built in such large mbers that the names did not correspond with e class letter at all. Thus, for example, the 'M' ass built between 1914 and 1917 had names ginning with 'M', 'N', 'O', 'P' and 'R'. It was parent that as the building programme acceler- ed from 1942 onwards, a similar situation would ise.

The 11th Flotilla was therefore initially allocated names such as *Pellew, Swallow* and *Tourmaline*, but subsequently it was decided to return to some semblance of alphabetical naming. Although there were still ships of the previous 'A' and 'B' classes in commission, all of the 'C' class had been transferred to Canada and renamed, and so a new series of names was selected using this initial. In fact it was realised that further orders for the standard Emergency destroyer design would be placed so that the first eight were given names beginning with 'Ca' and when orders were placed for three further flotillas they were given names beginning with 'Ch', 'Co' and 'Cr' respectively.

Altogether, 32 ships of the 'C' group were completed, although many did not commission until well after the end of hostilities in 1945. They served extensively with the Royal Navy in the postwar years, comparatively few being trans- ferred to foreign navies. Taking the Emergency War Programme from 1940, when the 'Q' and 'R' classes were ordered, to 1946, when the last of the 'C' group were completed, a total of 96 ships using an identical hull and machinery were built. Although they differed in detail, particularly in armament, they all retained the same basic layout and can really be considered as one class. Today they would be looked at as batches of the basic design. Thus the 'Q' and 'R' classes would be the original Batch I, the 'S' to 'W' classes which introduced the new gun mounting and revised bow shape would be Batch II, the 'Z' and 'Ca' classes would be a Batch III, while the remaining 'C' group could be considered as a Batch IV variant. Looked at in this light, the destroyer construction programme was an immense industrial under- taking, especially bearing in mind the other types

which were in production during the latter years of the war and which have not yet been considered. Of course the output of the British shipbuilding industry, impressive as it was, paled in comparison with the gigantic industrial might of the United States. Nevertheless it was a magnificent achievement and one which could not be repeated today given the individual complexity of modern ships and the closure of many famous shipyards.

As the 'C' group is not completely uniform, and as their careers differed, it will now be appropriate to consider each flotilla in turn.

rdered on 16 February 1942, this flotilla was
entical to the 'Z' class and in fact *Caprice* was
mpleted ahead of the first 'Z' class ship (*Myngs*)
ad ran trials in April 1944. Like the earlier class,
ere were delays in construction — not only due
equipment shortages, but also because of
amage to shipyards caused by enemy bombing.
S. White's yard at Cowes suffered particularly
adly in April and May of 1942, which delayed the
ying down of their two ships.

Designed armament was four 4.5in guns, one
in 40mm, and six or eight 20mm guns as well as
ght 21in torpedo tubes. However, availability
roblems meant that *Caprice* was completed with a
uadruple 2pdr (one of the last to be installed in a
ew build ship) instead of the twin 40mm
ounting.

All eight were completed by February 1945 and
ormed the 6th Destroyer Flotilla, initially with the
ome Fleet covering the Russian convoys. At the
ad of 1944 *Cassandra* was already engaged in
ese operations when she was hit by a torpedo
red from a U-Boat (11 December 1944). Her bow
as blown off and A gun disappeared. Following
aitial repairs at Kola Inlet, she arrived back in the
JK but was eventually transferred to Gibraltar in
aly 1945 for full repairs. This took over a year and
ae subsequently went into reserve in 1946.

The rest of the class were earmarked for service
the Far East and before sailing underwent
aodifications to suit them for service in that area.
a particular, several ships received single 2pdrs to
eplace some of the twin 20mm mountings as the
atter were considered unable to stop determined
amikaze attacks. By the time these modifications
ad been carried out and the Flotilla had
ssembled in Colombo as part of the Far East
leet, in late 1945, the war was over. One or two

ships took part in various mopping up operations
but all returned to the UK early in 1946 and were
laid up in reserve. In 1947 *Carysfort* briefly
commissioned for a training cruise to the
Mediterranean but was soon back in mothballs.

As will be related, the later C group destroyers
had a more advanced fire control system than
the 'Ca' class and consequently they were more
active over this period. However, in 1951 a Staff
Requirement was issued for the modernisation of
the 'Ca' class which would eventually result in their
return to service and prolong their lives beyond
that of their contemporaries.

Already, by 1945, the standard Emergency
Flotilla destroyer, as exemplified by the 'S' to 'Z'
classes as well as the 'C' group, was showing signs
of being outdated. However, production continued as newer designs were not then quite ready
for full scale production although, had the war
continued, the 'C' group would in any case have
been the last to be built to the traditional design.
One problem was that the basic 'J' class hull was
becoming too small to accommodate all the new
equipment which was being fitted to warships and
there was not sufficient space for the increased
manning required. Many new items, such as radar
or new HA directors, needed to be mounted high
up. This reduced stability margins and Captain's
reports indicated that the 'C' group ships were very
tender in this respect. Another consideration was
that the destroyers' traditional anti-submarine
armament, the depth charge, was no longer
considered an effective weapon system for use
against contemporary and future submarines. By
1945, most escorts were being fitted with the new
Squid AS mortar system which threw a 390lb
projectile up to 300yd ahead of the ship. The
importance of this was that it could be fired while
the ship still held the submarine in sonar contact,
making it a much more accurate system than
dropping depth charges as the ship passed over the
submarine's estimated position as contact was lost.
Until 1945, Squid had always been mounted on the
forecastle of the carrying ship but this was not
considered acceptable on destroyers as it would
displace one of the forward guns. Postwar
experience showed that Squid could be mounted
aft and safely fired forward over the bridge and
mast of a destroyer.

In the postwar era, the prime function of the
destroyer became the escort and support of the
carrier task forces which were intended to form the
core of the fleet. The main threats would be from
air and submarine attack, while the surface threat
appeared to have receded as the Soviet Navy was

not strong in that respect (although the postwar appearance of the 'Sverdlov' class cruisers caused a reappraisal in the 1950s). As originally built, the 'Ca' class were not suitable for this role but, unlike their predecessors, they were still included as part of the Royal Navy's total destroyer strength and were not listed as available for frigate conversion. This background was the reason for the modernisation requirement in 1951.

HMS *Carron* was taken out of reserve in 1953 for a modernisation at Chatham Dockyard which was to take over two years. *Cavendish* followed in January 1954, and the rest of the class followed over the next few years with *Caesar* and *Cassandra* not being completed until 1959.

The modernisation programme was quite extensive and started with the removal of much equipment in order to reduce topweight. This included the original bridge structure, all the old radar and sonar outfits together with the Mk I Type K director, 25 tons of cabling, one set of torpedo tubes, X gun and most of the light AA armament. The 4.5in guns were given RPC Mk V

Right:
An aerial view of HMS *Caesar* showing the layout of the ship after modernisation. On the after deckhouse can be seen the Squid mortars with the curved tracks for the bomb handling trolleys. Note also the Mk V twin 40mm gun with its STD just above.
Imperial War Museum

Below:
As modernised, the 'Ca' class were employed as fleet escorts. HMS *Cassandra* is shown in this role with the carrier *Victorious* in the background. The guns and torpedoes are trained to starboard.
Imperial War Museum

and were controlled by a new Mk 6M director carrying the twin antennae of the Type 275 radar. The bridge was rebuilt along the lines of the then current 'Daring' class destroyers with its distinctive angled faces (although still open in the traditional destroyer manner). The after deckhouse was extended forward to the remaining set of torpedo tubes. At the forward end of this was mounted a Mk V twin 40mm Bofors with an associated STD, while at the after end two Squid mortars and their handling gear were installed. Single 40mm guns were carried in the bridge wings.

A new lattice foremast carried a Type 293Q with its wide 'cheese' scanner and a Type 974/978 navigation radar was fitted below. A polemast extension carried UHF/DF and ESM aerials. The Squid magazine carried enough rounds for 10 double salvoes which were controlled by sonar Types 164/174.

On completion the final armament disposition was three 4.5in guns, four 40mm (two single, one twin), four 21in torpedo tubes, and two three-barrelled Squid AS mortars. In addition to the obvious external changes, there were improvements to the internal accommodation including new messing arrangements. One reason for the delay to the later ships was that the last four featured a further modification in that they were rebuilt with an enclosed frigate-type bridge which made life considerably easier for the duty watch on

the bridge but perhaps lacked the image demanded of traditional destroyer men!

Although *Carron* was the first to be modernised, she was not employed as a fully operational ship but was allocated to the Dartmouth Training Squadron. For this role she also lost B gun (leaving only two 4.5in) and an extra deckhouse was built forward of the bridge. Later she was completely disarmed and continued as a navigation training ship until laid up in 1963.

In the early 1960s, most of the remaining ships served in the Far East based at Singapore, initially forming the 8th Destroyer Squadron. But later policy dictated the formation of mixed escort squadrons consisting of various types of destroyers and frigates offering a whole range of specialised capabilities. Consequently the 8th Destroyer Squadron was disbanded, the ships going to various escort groups operating in the Far East. Many, including *Cassandra, Carysfort* and *Caesar*, were involved in the Indonesian Confrontation while others later took part in the Beira Patrol off Mozambique following Rhodesia's illegal declaration of independence and the resulting oil sanctions.

One of the themes running through destroyer development during and after the war was the continual updating of the close range AA armament. During the war most ships had a multiple 2pdr which was gradually replaced by the radar controlled Hazemeyer twin 40mm mounting. This in turn was supplanted (on larger destroyers) by the STAAG twin 40mm mounting which will be described in the next chapter. However, even this was eventually to be overtaken by the introduction of a short range surface-to-air missile system light enough to be mounted on a destroyer — Seacat.

The history of this simple, but effective, system will also be dealt with later in this book, but it was widely adopted during the mid-1960s as the Royal Navy's standard close range air defence system. In addition to being fitted to new and modernised frigates, it was also intended to arm most of the operational destroyer fleet and consequently some of the 'Ca' class were modified during this period. This involved the removal of the Mk V twin 40mm and its STD from after superstructure and the erection of a high deckhouse at the forward end which contained the missile handling arrangements. A quadruple missile launcher stood on the former gun position and a GWS 20 missile director was carried atop the new deckhouse, offset to port.

The removal of the twin 40mm and the superstructure alterations were progressively incorporated in *Cavendish, Cavalier, Carysfort, Cambrian* and *Caprice* as they underwent routine refits between 1963 and 1966. However, in the end, only *Cavalier* and *Caprice* actually received the Seacat missile system in 1966, landing their remaining torpedo tubes to compensate for the extra topweight. The other three ships carried a single Mk 7 40mm Bofors mounting, intended as a temporary measure, and never received their Seacats.

The mid-1960s were a period of contraction for the UK armed forces and the Navy suffered as much as any. Withdrawals from the East of Suez area and the decision to run down the carrier fleet meant that fewer destroyers were required. Consequently *Cassandra, Cambrian, Caesar, Cavendish* and *Carysfort* all paid off in the last half of the decade and were scrapped shortly afterwards.

This left only *Cavalier* and *Caprice*. The latter's last operational commission ended in 1969 but she continued in service as a seagoing training ship based at Devonport until 1974 when she was laid up, although not scrapped until 1979. *Cavalier* should have paid off in 1968 but a shortage of escort vessels resulted in a further two-year commission in Home and Mediterranean waters. During this time she took part in a race with HMS *Rapid* (a surviving 'R' class which had been converted to a frigate) to establish which ship should hold the unofficial title of 'Fastest Ship in the Fleet'. This race, held on 6 July 1971 off the Firth of Forth, was run over 2hr. At the end of this period HMS *Cavalier* was the winner — but only by a margin of a few yards! Average speed was 31.8kt.

The ship paid off in July 1972 and since then, as a result of a long campaign, money was raised to save her from the breakers so that she could become a museum ship, representing the scores of similar destroyers which have long since passed away after a glorious history. Unfortunately, the early hopes were not realised in full and, although HMS *Cavalier* still exists as a museum ship, she has been shuttled around from one port to another as various concerns found the cost of her upkeep too great. Initially she was moved to Southampton, where she eventually opened to the public in 1982, but since then she moved first to a Marina site at Brighton and then in 1987 to Hebburn-on-Tyne where it is intended that she will become the focus of a shipbuilding and maritime museum complex to be set up in the area. It is to be hoped that she has found her final resting place.

The only destroyer of World War 2 origin still in existence in the United Kingdom, HMS *Cavalier* now lies moored in the River Tyne where she will be the centrepiece of a new museum complex. *Author*

Name	No	Laid Down	Launched	Completed	Builder	Yard	Remarks	
Caesar	D07	03/04/43	12/02/44	05/10/44	J. Brown	Clydebank	Arr Blyth for scrap	06/01/67
Cambrian	D85	14/08/42	10/12/43	17/07/44	Scotts	Greenock	Towed Briton Ferry for scrap	03/09/71
Caprice	D01	28/09/43	16/09/42	05/04/44	Yarrow	Scotstoun	Scrapped Queenborough	11/79
Carron	D30	26/11/42	28/03/44	06/11/44	Scotts	Greenock	Arr Inverkeithing for scrap	04/04/67
Carysfort	D25	12/05/43	25/07/44	20/02/45	J. S. White	Cowes	Sold J. Cashmore for scrap	23/10/70
Cassandra	D10	30/01/43	29/11/43	28/07/44	Yarrow	Scotstoun	Arr Inverkeithing for scrap	28/04/67
Cavalier	D73	28/02/43	07/04/44	22/11/44	J. S. White	Cowes	Preserved as museum ship, Tyne	1987
Cavendish	D15	19/05/43	12/04/44	13/12/44	J. Brown	Clydebank	Arr Blyth for scrap	17/08/67

Data:	'Ca' class, HMS *Cavalier* (1946)		**Data:**	HMS *Caprice* (1959)
Displacement (tons):	1,710 standard, 2,530 full load		**Displacement** (tons):	2,020 standard, 2,600 full load
Length/Beam (ft):	363 (oa)/35.75		**Length/Beam** (ft):	As built
Draught (ft):	10 (light), 14.5 (full load)		**Draught** (ft):	As built
Armament:	4×single 4.5in, 1×Hazemeyer Mk IV twin 40mm mounting, 4×single 2pdr, 8×21in torpedo tubes, depth charges		**Armament:**	3×single 4.5in, 1×Mk V twin 40mm mounting, 2×single 40mm, 4×21in torpedo tubes, 2×Squid AS mortars
Radars:	Types 293, 291, 285, 282		**Radars:**	Types 293 P, 275, 974
Machinery:	As 'R' and later classes		**Machinery:**	As 'R' and later classes
Speed/Range:	32kt/1,400nm @ 32kt		**Speed/Range:**	32kt/2,800nm @ 20kt
Oil Fuel (tons):	615		**Oil Fuel** (tons):	580
Complement:	186		**Complement:**	192

'Ch' Class Destroyers — *Chaplet, Charity, Chequers, Cheviot, Chevron, Chieftain, Childers, Chivalrous*

This group of ships were basically similar to the preceding 'Ca' and 'Z' classes with the important difference that they introduced remote power control to the main armament which was controlled by a Mk VI director equipped with Type 275 radar. With this combination they were capable of engaging targets in 'blindfire' conditions with ranges and bearings accurately determined by radar and the guns automatically laid and trained by the fire control system. This was a major advance on previous destroyers but there was a heavy price to pay. For a start, severe delays in the supply of the Mk VI directors meant that none of

these ships were commissioned before the end of the war despite having been ordered in July 1942. The other problem was that RPC and the director added to the already worrying excess topweight of this class, RPC alone adding an extra 7 or 8 tons. Since the design of the original 'Q' class (which was basically the same ship), new and extra equipment had added 170 tons at upper deck level and this was now affecting stability to such an extent that measures had to be taken to alleviate the situation. Standard displacement had risen to 1,900 tons compared with 1,710 tons for the 'S' to 'Z' and 'Ca' classes.

The most obvious result was the deletion of one set of torpedo tubes, but other modifications included the use of a smaller searchlight (a 20in mounted forward instead of the traditional 44in carried aft), halving depth charge stowage to 48 dropped in five instead of 10-charge patterns, single hand-operated 20mm guns replacing twin powered mountings on the signal deck and the removal of Arctic heating arrangements. The increasing range of electronic equipment to be carried caused further difficulties, but most ships were completed with Type 293 on the foremast and Type 291 on a short mainmast, while gunnery sets included Type 275 on the director and Type 282 on the Bofors twin 40mm. As with earlier classes, the final light AA armament varied with 2pdr guns replacing some of the twin 20mm mountings.

Internally the ships were cramped as standard complement had risen to over 200, with up to 240 on the flotilla leaders (Chequers and Childers).

Below:
The 'Ch' class introduced the Mk VI director and RPC for the main armament. To compensate for the extra topweight it was necessary to land one set of torpedo tubes as shown in this view of HMS Chequers in 1947. Imperial War Museum

Bottom:
HMS Charity at Portsmouth in 1955. Light AA armament consists of one twin and four single 40mm guns, while one of the after 4.5in guns has been removed to enable two Squid mortars to be mounted. Wright and Logan

Conditions were worsened by the provision of extra equipment to suit the ships for tropical service including additional fan vents, water purifiers and cookers, as well as additional machinery and electrical equipment. Many of the crew could only bed down on top of lockers. Altogether this class showed that the limits of the basic 'J' class hull, designed well before the war, had been well and truly met. In ordinary times a new design would have been introduced much earlier, but war conditions made this impossible.

Nevertheless, the 'Ch' class (and the following 16 identical ships of the 'Co' and 'Cr' classes) formed an important part of the Royal Navy's postwar destroyer fleet. Almost all of the 'Ch' class were completed by the end of 1945 (with the exception of Chieftain and Chivalrous which completed early in 1946) and formed the 14th (later renumbered 1st) Destroyer Squadron in the Mediterranean, remaining active for the rest of the decade. During this time they were unaltered except that the close range AA armament was standardised as one twin and four single 40mm guns.

In 1950 the squadron split up and Childers, Cheviot and Chaplet returned home, being replaced by 'Loch' class frigates in an attempt to increase the ASW capability of the Mediterranean Fleet. Charity was dispatched to the Far East where she reinforced the 8th Destroyer Flotilla for operations off Korea and did not finally pay off into reserve until 1955.

Chequers, Chevron, Chieftain and Chivalrous

Above:
HMS *Childers* off Gibraltar in the early 1950s. The Mk VI Director is clearly visible above the bridge. Note that X gun and the Mk V twin 40mm have been removed. *Skyfotos*

remained in the Mediterranean with occasional deployments in other areas. For example, in July 1951 the four ships were dispatched to the Persian Gulf to relieve the cruiser *Euryalus*. Even with peacetime complements, conditions aboard must have been extremely trying in the Gulf area and the crews must have been pleased to return to their normal area of operations later in the year. In 1952 the Squadron visited Barcelona in company with the light carrier HMS *Glory*, the first official visit by the Royal Navy to Spain since the Civil War in 1937-38. In the mid-1950s some of the ships were laid up in reserve but were recalled to the Mediterranean in 1956 during the Suez Crisis. Among these were *Chieftain* and *Chevron*.

Few of the 'Ch' group were modernised along the lines of the earlier 'Ca' group, mainly because the were already equipped with RPC for the main armament and carried a Mk 6 Director. However, in 1954 most were given an interim modernisation which involved the removal of X mounting and the addition of two Squid mortars together with their associated ammunition handling gear. *Chaplet* and *Chieftain* were also equipped for minelaying but in this role the torpedo tubes and Y gun would have to be landed to maintain stability.

Two ships were sold to the Pakistan Navy,

Chivalrous in 1954 and *Charity* in 1958, being renamed *Taimur* and *Jehan* respectively. *Chivalrous* was returned to the Royal Navy and eventually scrapped in 1961 but *Charity*, which had been given the interim, modernisation before the sale, enjoyed a longer career and was not finally scrapped until 1982.

Cheviot and *Chaplet* were the last ships of the group to remain active in the Royal Navy. The former served a commission in the Far East as part of the 8th Destroyer Squadron between 1956 and 1959 when she returned to the UK and paid off. Subsequently she served as a harbour training ship at Rosyth until sold off in 1962. *Chaplet* was active until 1961 as part of the Devonport Local Squadron and was then laid up until sold for scrapping in 1965. In the meantime the remaining ships had already been laid up and were scrapped between 1961 and 1969.

Data:	'CO' class, HMS *Constance* (1954)
Displacement (tons):	1,710 standard, 2,640 full load
Length/Beam (ft):	363 (oa)/35.75
Draught (ft):	16 (full load)
Armament:	3×4.5in on single RP50 Mk V mountings, 1×Mk V twin 40mm mountings, 5×single 40mm, 4×21in torpedo tubes, depth charges
Radars:	Types 293, 291, 275, 974
Machinery:	As 'R' and later classes
Speed/Range:	32kt/2,800nm @ 20kt
Oil Fuel (tons):	580
Complement:	241

'Co' Class Destroyers — *Cockade, Comet, Comus, Concord, Consort, Constance, Contest, Cossack*

The 13th Emergency Flotilla were exact repeats of the preceding 'Ch' class with the notable exception of *Contest* which was the first all-welded destroyer to be built for the Royal Navy. The ship was built by J. S. White at Cowes whose yard had been seriously damaged by an air attack and was being rebuilt with new fabrication shops to suit this method of construction. Welded construction was already widely used by American shipbuilders and many wartime German destroyers were also built in this way, but British construction practice had persisted with the traditional riveted construction throughout the war to avoid disruption to the various building programmes.

Slow production of fire control equipment again resulted in delays and last of the class, *Concord*, was not completed until the end of 1946. The first five (*Cockade, Contest, Cossack, Comet, Constance*) were completed with a light AA armament consisting of a twin 40mm Hazemeyer mounting amidships, two single 2pdrs abaft the funnel and a single 20mm in the bridge wings. The remainder had a Mk V twin 40mm mounting instead of the Hazemeyer and single 40mm guns abaft the funnel instead of the 2pdr. The earlier ships were later altered to conform with this arrangement.

Once in commission the entire class was dispatched to the Far East where they formed the 8th Destroyer Squadron. *Cockade, Comet* and *Contest* returned to the UK in 1948 for a refit but, with the exception of *Comet*, rejoined the remainder to serve throughout most of the Korean War. *Consort* was one of the first ships to see action when she was involved in the *Amethyst* incident on the Yangtse river in 1949. Having been relieved as Nanking guardship by *Amethyst*, she later tried to assist the frigate when it came under fire from Chinese Nationalist forces on the north bank of the river. In this action *Consort* was hit several times and a number of her crew were killed or wounded, forcing the destroyer to withdraw down river. *Amethyst* later managed to escape down river where she was met by a force of British ships including the cruiser *London* and destroyer *Concord*.

When the Korean War broke out in 1950, the 8th Destroyer Squadron was heavily committed, mainly in escorting the various light fleet carriers operating off the coast. However, they were also involved in support bombardment missions in support of United Nations forces ashore, usually accompanying cruisers such as *Belfast, Jamaica* and *Ceylon*. For example in August 1950 *Cossack* and *Cockade*, accompanied by *Charity* and the

Below left:
As completed, HMS *Comet* wears a wartime camouflage pattern with a dark blue/grey panel on a light grey hull. *Imperial War Museum*

Bottom:
The 'Co' class served extensively in the Far East as the 8th Destroyer Squadron and played an important part in the Korean War. HMS *Cockade* is shown coming alongside an American landing craft in ice packed waters off the Korean Coast in 1950. *Imperial War Museum*

Top:
HMS *Cockade* as completed. She shows the standard configuration of these ships as built with Type 293 radar at the top of the lattice mast, Type 291 on the after pole mast, Type 275 on the Mk VI director and Type 282 on the Hazemeyer amidships. *Yarrow*

Above:
HMS *Comet* following an interim modernisation and equipped for minelaying. In this view she is actually carrying a complement of mines, visible on the stern, and consequently the torpedoes and after gun have been removed to compensate.
Imperial War Museum

cruisers *Belfast* and *Ceylon*, carried out several bombardments off Inchon. Even after the Korean War there was plenty of action and in 1955 *Comus* was engaged in a bombardment of Communist forces in Malaya in a big operation which also involved air and land forces.

None of the class was sold abroad and *Constance* and *Comus* were listed for disposal in 1955,

eventually being scrapped in 1956 and 1958 respectively. Of the others, *Comet* and *Contest* were given the interim modernisation and fitted for minelaying, subsequently serving in Home waters with the 6th Destroyer Squadron until the late 1950s when they paid off and were later scrapped in 1962 and 1960.

The remaining four ships (*Cockade, Cossack Consort, Concord*) remained in the Far East until 1957 (*Cossack* until 1959) when they returned to the UK and paid off into reserve. All were scrapped in the early 1960s.

The 'Ch' and 'Co' destroyers gave valuable service to the Royal Navy in the period 1945-59 but, as they were almost all deployed to overseas stations, their contribution has tended to be overlooked and photographs of these ships are less common than the 'Ca' group and other classes which were more often at home and in the public eye. Nevertheless, they were almost continually in commission and performed sterling work, particularly in Korea.

'Cr' Class Destroyers — *Creole, Crescent, Crispin, Cromwell, Crown, Croziers, Crusader, Crystal*

This was the final flotilla of the Emergency War Programme to be built, although there were plans too for another batch of eight ships which would have been the 'Ce' Group. However, contracts for the latter were cancelled at an early stage in favour of the 'Weapon' Class which will be described in the next chapter. The 'Cr' class were all completed in 1945-46 but only two ever served with the Royal Navy — *Creole* and *Crispin*. Both served with the 3rd Training Squadron based at Londonderry and in 1948 their B gun removed and replaced with a deckhouse. However, their RN careers were short-lived and by 1954 both were laid up in reserve. In 1958 the two ships were sold to Pakistan and renamed *Alamgir* and *Janangir* respectively. Before being handed over the deckhouse forward was removed and the B gun

Below:
HMS *Crystal*, as completed in 1946, had a light AA armament of one twin 40mm Hazemeyer mounting, two single 40mm abaft the funnel, and single 20mm in the bridge wings. *Yarrow*

Bottom:
In company with three other ships of the class, *Crystal* was transferred to the Norwegian Navy. She is shown here as the *K. N. M. Stavanger* in 1950 and is unaltered from her original profile.
Wright and Logan

replaced. Two Squid mortars were fitted aft, replacing X gun, and light AA armament consisted of one twin and four single 40mm mountings. As with previous sales to Pakistan, these ships outlived their RN contemporaries and were not scrapped until 1982.

Two more ships, *Crescent* and *Crusader*, were transferred to the RCN on completion. *Crescent* was converted in 1954-56 along the lines of the British Type 15 (the only ship of the 32 'C' group destroyers to be rebuilt as a fast ASW frigate) although there were a number of differences, notably the positioning of the twin 4in gun which was mounted forward of the bridge. A twin 3in mounting was carried aft and single 40mm guns abreast the foremast. Two Limbo mortars were carried but one of these was later replaced by a variable depth sonar, the Canadians being in the forefront of the development of this equipment. *Crusader* was not substantially altered although she was used as an experimental ship for ASW purposes for many years and was a trials ship for the VDS. She was scrapped in 1965 and *Crescent* followed in 1971.

The remaining four ships were transferred to the Norwegian Navy in 1945-47. *Cromwell, Crown, Croziers* and *Crystal* were renamed *Bergen, Oslo, Trondheim* and *Stavanger* respectively. During their service lives they were almost unaltered and were laid up and scrapped between 1961 and 1967.

Above:
HMS *Crispin* was one of only two 'Cr' class to serve with the Royal Navy. B gun has been removed and a deckhouse erected in its place for training purposes. *Real Photos (S2120)*

Bottom:
Crescent was transferred to the Canadian Navy in 1945 and was later converted along the lines of the British Type 15 frigate, the only 'C' Group destroyer to be so modified. She differs from British frigate conversions in that the 4in gun is forward of the bridge, a twin 3in/50cal is mounted aft and the bridge structure is larger. *Real Photos (N853)*

The 'C' group were, numerically, among the most important of the destroyers available to the Royal Navy in the postwar era and saw widespread service. Unlike the earlier classes they were not earmarked for conversion to frigates and retained their destroyer lines to the end. However, they represented the final stage of the medium-sized fleet destroyer and at the time of their completion were already overloaded and cramped. It was obvious by the middle of World War 2 that larger destroyers were required. Their development is described in the following chapter.

Name	No	Laid Down	Launched	Completed	Builder	Yard	Remarks	
Chaplet	D52	29/04/43	18/07/44	24/08/45	Thornycroft	Woolston	Arr Blyth for scrap	06/11/65
Charity	D29	09/07/43	30/11/44	19/11/45	Thornycroft	Woolston	PN 1958. Scrapped	1982
Chequers	D61	04/05/43	30/10/44	28/09/45	Scotts	Greenock	Arr Newport for scrap	23/07/66
Cheviot	D90	27/04/43	02/05/44	11/12/44	Alex Stephens	Linthouse	Arr Inverkeithing for scrap	22/10/62
Chevron	D51	18/03/43	23/02/44	23/08/45	Alex Stephens	Linthouse	Arr Inverkeithing for scrap	12/69
Chieftain	D36	27/06/43	26/02/45	07/03/46	Scotts	Greenock	Arr Sunderland for scrap	20/03/61
Childers	D91	27/11/43	27/02/45	19/12/45	Denny	Dunbarton	Arr La Spezia for scrap	22/09/63
Chivalrous	D21	27/11/43	22/06/45	13/05/46	Denny	Dunbarton	PN 1954. Scrapped	1961
Cockade	D34	11/03/43	07/03/44	29/09/45	Yarrow	Scotstoun	Arr Newport for scrap	08/64
Comet	D26	14/06/43	22/06/44	06/06/45	Yarrow	Scotstoun	Arr Troon for scrap	23/10/62
Comus	D20	21/08/43	14/03/45	08/07/46	Thornycroft	Woolston	Arr Newport for scrap	12/11/58
Concord	D03	18/11/43	14/05/45	20/12/46	Thornycroft	Woolston	Arr Inverkeithing for scrap	22/10/62
Consort	D76	26/05/43	19/10/44	19/03/46	Alex Stephens	Linthouse	Arr Swansea for scrap	15/03/61
Constance	D71	18/03/43	22/08/44	31/12/45	Vickers Armstrong	Tyne	Arr Inverkeithing for scrap	08/03/56
Contest	D48	01/11/43	16/12/44	09/11/45	J. S. White	Cowes	Arr Grays, Essex for scrap	15/03/61
Cossack	D57	18/03/43	10/05/44	04/09/45	Vickers Armstrong	Tyne	Arr Troon for scrap	01/03/61
Crispin	D168	01/02/44	23/06/45	10/07/46	J. S. White	Cowes	PN 1958. Scrapped	1982
Creole	D82	03/08/44	22/11/45	14/10/46	J. S. White	Cowes	PN 1958. Scrapped	1982
Cromwell	R35	24/11/43	06/08/45	16/09/46	Scotts	Greenock	RNN 1946. Scrapped	1967
Crescent	226	16/09/43	20/07/44	21/09/45	J. Brown	Clydebank	RCN 1945. Type 15. Scrapped	1971
Crown	R46	16/01/44	19/12/44	17/05/47	Scotts	Greenock	RNN 1945. Scrapped Grimstad	07/68
Croziers	R27	26/10/43	19/09/44	30/11/45	Yarrow	Scotstoun	RNN 1945. Arr Belgium for scrap	12/61
Crusader	228	15/11/43	05/10/44	26/11/45	J. Brown	Clydebank	RCN 1945. Scrapped	1965
Crystal	R38	13/01/44	12/02/45	06/02/46	Yarrow	Scotstoun	RNN 1946. Scrapped	1967

4 'Battles', 'Weapons' and 'Darings'

'Battle' Class Destroyers (1942) — *Armada, Barfleur, Cadiz, Camperdown, Finisterre, Gabbard, Gravelines, Hogue, Lagos, St James, St Kitts, Saintes, Sluys, Solebay, Trafalgar, Vigo*

The early years of World War 2 had shown that British destroyers were ill-equipped to deal with concentrated air attacks and had suffered heavy losses as a result. Various temporary expedients had been tried out including the substitution of 4in guns for torpedo tubes, improved close range AA armament, introducing the 4in gun as main armament (as in the 'L' and some 'O' and 'P' class ships) and increasing the elevation of the 4.7in and 4.5in mountings to 50° and then 55°. However, none of these did much to improve matters and in most cases were not allied to a specially designed, radar assisted, fire control system.

In 1941 consideration of these problems gave rise to a naval staff requirement for a new class of large destroyer which would be fitted with a new HA twin 4.7in mounting with a HA control system. Various sketch designs were produced to meet the specification and considerable debate took place concerning the type and disposition of the armament. At an early stage it was decided that the main battery would consist of two twin 4.7in mountings set forward thus allowing both

Below:
The early 'Battle' class were intended to carry a 4in gun abaft the funnel as shown in this view of HMS *Camperdown*. The gun was later removed and replaced by two 40mm Bofors. *Author's Collection*

turrets to concentrate on a single target. Arcs of fire would be increased by positioning the bridge structure further aft than normal. The close range AA armament would consist of four twin 40mm Bofors disposed to give all-round overlapping arcs of fire and these would be supplemented by six single 20mm guns. Two quadruple sets of torpedo tubes would be carried. A new feature would be the use of stabilisers to give a stable platform for AA gunnery. Although this had been tried out on the 'Black Swan' class frigates, this was the first time it would be employed in destroyers.

With these parameters accepted a sketch design was submitted at the end of 1941 showing a standard displacement of 2,280 tons and carrying 700 tons of oil fuel giving a range of 7,700 miles at 12kt. The sketch design was approved in October 1941 and orders for 16 ships (two flotillas) were placed under the 1942 programme. As they were considerably larger than the standard destroyers and were regarded in some circles as replacements for the 'Tribal' class which had already suffered heavy losses, the alphabetic naming system was abandoned and the ships were named after famous battles (both land and sea). Thus this first group became known as the 1942 'Battle' class.

The placing of orders did not halt the continued work on the design and at this stage the naval staff altered their ideas as to the disposition of the main

armament and now decided that a turret fore and aft would be a better arrangement. Many reasons were given, perhaps the most logical being that a single hit was unlikely to put both turrets out of action, but by this time plans were too advanced to contemplate a change of this nature. Other calls for changes included one for the addition of a third twin 4.7in turret to increase the gun armament as it was felt in some quarters that the design was underarmed for its size. One far-sighted Admiral questioned the continuing need for a heavy torpedo armament in view of the advent of radar and the erosion of the destroyer's traditional speed advantage over its planned targets. Neither of these proposals was incorporated although the addition of a third turret would receive further consideration at a later date.

However, one change was made and that was to standardise on the 4.5in gun instead of the original 4.7in Mk XI as fitted to the 'L' and 'M' classes. Another change was the addition of a single 4in gun abaft the funnel which was mainly intended to fire starshells for illuminating targets at night but could also supplement the AA fire and provide some measure of fire on the after arcs (although not directly astern).

The twin 40mm guns would be on Hazemeyer stabilised mountings fitted with Type 282 radar. These were mounted one on either beam between the torpedo tubes and two en echelon on the after deckhouse. Four single 20mm were to be carried, one just forward of the bridge, two in the bridge wings and one on the quarterdeck. Due to delays in completion of the early ships, the 20mm arrangements were initially altered to twin mountings in each position and these, in turn, were later replaced by either single 40mm or 2pdr guns.

The delays in completion were, as in other classes, due to the late delivery of the Mk VI directors and fire control systems. Originally it was expected that 18 of these, each incorporating the Type 275 radar, would be available by the end of 1944. Of these, four were earmarked for the battleship *Anson* and the first destroyer unit would be fitted to a 'C' class ship in August 1944.

Thus the first 'Battle' class destroyer, HMS *Barfleur*, was completed by Swan Hunter in mid-1944, but by August her DCT had not been delivered. Consequently the ship was commissioned and ran trials in September but then returned to the Tyne to await delivery and installation of the director. *Trafalgar* was likewise affected and spent several months laid up in the Tyne during 1944.

The 4in gun amidships was soon recognised to be of limited usefulness and reports from the Pacific indicated that it would be preferable to mount two single 40mm guns instead. This change was duly introduced and only *Armada*, *Barfleur*,

Camperdown and *Hogue* were completed with the 4in, and even on these ships it was eventually removed and replaced by two Bofors. The other ships completed before the end of 1945 (*Finisterre*, *Lagos*, *Solebay* and *Trafalgar*) were armed with the full outfit of 40mm guns including the four Hazemeyer mountings giving a total of 14 Bofors — the heaviest light AA armament carried by any British destroyer and a far cry from the desperate days of 1940. All ships were completed with a lattice mast instead of the tripod shown on the original plans. Radar outfit consisted of a Type 293 on the foremast and a Type 291 air warning on a polemast aft, as well as the Type 275 and 282 gunnery radars. Other electronic equipment included HF/DF and various IFF transponders and receivers on the foremast.

With an overall length of 379ft, the 'Battle' class were just 2ft longer than the earlier 'Tribals' but the beam was increased by just under 4ft to a total of 40ft 3in. At a standard displacement of 2,315 tons, the 'Battles' were almost 400 tons heavier, and over 700 tons heavier at full load. There was less emphasis on speed and the 'Battles' made only 31kt at full load (compared with 32½kt for the 'Tribal' class) despite an increase to 50,000shp by the use of higher pressure boilers.

The first eight ships were destined to form the 19th Destroyer Flotilla with the British Pacific Fleet but only *Barfleur* actually saw any war service against Japan and was present at the surrender ceremony in Tokyo Bay on 3 September 1945. After the end of hostilities *Armada*, *Camperdown*, *Hogue*, *Lagos* and *Trafalgar* eventually reached the Far East but in 1947 all six ships returned home and were laid up in reserve. The remaining two ships, *Solebay* and *Finisterre*, did not go to the Far East and the latter was employed as a gunnery and training ship. *Solebay* joined the Home Fleet as leader of the 5th Destroyer Flotilla which consisted of most of the remaining 'Battle' class completed in 1946.

These latter ships introduced a change in the light AA armament. The four Hazemeyer mountings with their Type 282 radar were replaced by two new twin 40mm mountings of British design. The Hazemeyer always suffered from mechanical unreliability and, although it carried its own fire control equipment, the Type 282 only gave range information on the target. The new British design, known as the Stabilised Tachymetric Anti-Aircraft Gun (STAAG), was actually even more complex and was no more reliable. However, it used the Type 262 centimetric aerial with a small dish aerial which was capable of locking on to and tracking a target. Thus the fire control system was constantly updated with target range and bearing, and the rate of change of both these parameters, so that it could automatically train and elevate the guns as

71

the target moved. The whole installation weighed 17 tons (compared with only 7 tons of the Hazemeyer). Consequently, only two mountings could be carried and these were positioned en echelon on the after deckhouse where they commanded the best arcs of fire.

A one-off armament variation occurred when HMS *Saintes* was completed with a new twin 4.5in turret on B mounting in front of the bridge. This was the RP41 Mk VI mounting which was a completely new design offering improved ammunition handling and increased rate of fire due to the semi-automatic breech action. The gun house was basically a cube with rounded edges and later became a familiar fixture on postwar frigates and the 'Daring' class destroyers, and is currently still carried aboard unmodified 'Leander' class frigates.

Like the 19th Flotilla, the 5th only consisted of six ships (*Solebay, Cadiz, Gabbard, St James, St Kitts, Sluys*) to reduce running costs. *Gravelines* and *Vigo*, completed in the latter half of 1946, went straight in reserve as they were not immediately required in the peacetime navy and there was, in any case, the beginning of a serious manning problem which was to reach its peak in 1948. However, in 1949 they were finally commissioned when the 3rd Destroyer Flotilla, consisting of *Saintes, Armada, Vigo* and *Gravelines*, was formed to replace *Troubridge* and the remaining 'V' class in the Mediterranean. In the next few years there was some interchange of ships between the 5th and 3rd Destroyer Squadrons (as they were now redesignated) and at the Coronation Review in 1953 *Solebay, Cadiz* and

St James represented the 5th DS as part of the Home Fleet while *Barfleur* and *St Kitts* were among ships from the Mediterranean Fleet. Other 1942 'Battles' present were *Trafalgar* and *Camperdown* from the Reserve Fleet, and *Finisterre* from Portsmouth Command.

In 1953, after the Review, the 5th DS disbanded and the six ships concerned went into reserve pending a refit. By late 1956 the only operational ships were *Armada, Barfleur, St Kitts* with the 3rd DS in the Mediterranean (where they took part in the Suez operation) and *Vigo*, which had replaced

Below:
This view from the open bridge of a 'Battle' class destroyer conveys a little of the flavour of destroyer operations. *Imperial War Museum*

Above right:
Depth charges explode in the wake of HMS *Finisterre* as she takes part in exercises in the English Channel. *Imperial War Museum*

Right:
HMS *Gabbard* as completed without the 4in gun and with two STAAG mountings instead of the Hazemeyers. The black funnel band indicates that she is acting as a divisional leader of the 5th Destroyer Squadron. *Skyfotos*

Below right:
HMS *Camperdown* at Malta in 1961 while serving with the 1st Destroyer Squadron. In the background are two ex-US 'Fletcher' class destroyers transferred to the Greek Navy. *Imperial War Museum*

Finisterre as a gunnery training ship. The others were in reserve or undergoing refit.

During the early 1950s most of the 1942 'Battles' underwent some modernisation to achieve standardisation of armament. Those which had originally carried the Hazemeyer mountings received two STAAGs in lieu and the quarterdeck 40mm, where mounted, was removed and replaced by a Squid AS mortar, the after deckhouse being extended to form a mortar handling room. Internally the fire control system was updated, although the Mk 6 director with Type 275 radar was retained, and new sonars were fitted.

In the latter half of the 1950s the 'Battles' continued to give good service. The 'Ch' class destroyers of the 1st DS were replaced in 1957 by *Solebay*, *Hogue*, and *Lagos*. Initially they served in the Mediterranean but in 1959 deployed to the Far East where *Hogue's* career was abruptly terminated by an unfortunate collision with the Indian cruiser *Mysore*. Although not sunk, she was towed to Singapore and laid up until scrapped in 1962. In 1960 a new 1st Destroyer Squadron was formed from the remaining ships of the previous 1st and 3rd (*Solebay*, *Finisterre*, *Saintes* and *Camperdown*) and operated in home and Mediterranean waters. In 1961 the last three named were among a considerable force of Royal Navy ships dispatched to the Persian Gulf to assist the state of Kuwait which was under threat of invasion from Iraq. The squadron was disbanded in 1962 when the ships were laid up in reserve.

One 'Battle' given a new lease of life was *Trafalgar*. Laid up since 1947, she was refitted and commissioned in May 1958 as leader of the 7th DS. She served in the Mediterranean during the Lebanon crisis that year, the following year found her off Iceland engaged in fishery protection

Top left:
HMS *Trafalgar* laid up at Portsmouth in 1968. The two STAAG mountings aft have been replaced by two Mk V twin 40mm mountings during her 1958 refit. *C. and S. Taylor*

Above left:
The USS *Buck*, launched in March 1945, was one of the 'Allen M. Sumner' class which were an American design roughly contemporary with the 'Battles'. On a displacement of 2,200 tons they originally shipped six 5in guns, a hefty light AA armament and 10 21in torpedo tubes. In this postwar view, *Buck* now carries three quadruple 40mm mountings and only one set of torpedo tubes between the funnels. *Real Photos (N39)*

Left:
HMS *Sluys* alongside at Vosper's Southampton yard in May 1968 where she is undergoing an extensive refit after being sold to the Iranian Navy and renamed *Artemiz*. *Maritime Photo Library*

duties, and she continued in service at home and abroad until 1963.

Gravelines and *St James* commenced a modernisation refit in 1958 but these were stopped a few months later and the ships laid up, unfortunately not before £436,000 had been spent on them. Both were subsequently scrapped as were most of the 1942 'Battles' between 1961 and 1972. Exceptions to this were *Cadiz* and *Gabbard* which, in 1956, were sold to Pakistan. These two ships were refitted in 1956-57 before being handed over to their new owners and being renamed *Khaibar* and *Badr* respectively. During the refit the two STAAG mountings aft were replaced by two Mk V twin 40mm mountings controlled by two STDs carried forward of the guns, this modification being made to most of the remaining RN ships around this time. *Khaibar* was sunk in 1971 during the Indo-Pakistan war but *Badr* was still on the Pakistan Navy List as late as 1985.

The only other 1942 'Battle' to be sold abroad was HMS *Sluys* which was transferred to Iran in 1966, subsequently undergoing a three-year modernisation at Vosper Thornycroft's Southampton Yard. Renamed *Artemiz*, she recommissioned in 1970 with a substantially altered profile. The 4.5in guns forward were retained but the close range AA armament now consisted of four single 40mm guns and a quadruple Seacat missile launcher on the after end of a new deckhouse structure which extended from the base of the funnel to the quarterdeck. A new plated mainmast carried the parabolic aerial of a Plessey AWS 1 long range search radar while a new, fully enclosed bridge surmounted the forward superstructure. During 1975-76 the ship underwent a refit at Cape Town and was fitted with surface-to-surface missile launchers. She is still in existence although believed to be non-operational. The 16 'Battle' class built under the 1942 programme provided the backbone of the Royal Navy's destroyer force in the two decades following the end of the war. They were fine looking ships and their inception probably marked the point at which the prime function of a destroyer was seen to be the aerial defence of the fleet or task force which it was escorting. In this sense they started the line of development which has resulted in today's anti-aircraft missile equipped destroyers. However, they were generally accepted to be underarmed for their size and, although steps were proposed to rectify this, they compared unfavourably with the contemporary 'Allen M. Sumner' and 'Gearing' class destroyers which carried six 5in guns plus torpedoes and a good light AA armament on a similar displacement. The grouping of the main armament forward led to an unbalanced design and a more even disposition might have produced a more effective ship.

'Battle' Class Destroyers (1943) — *Agincourt, Alamein, Aisne, Barrosa, Matapan, Corunna, Dunkirk, Jutland*

Between March and June 1943, orders for a further 24 'Battle' class destroyers were placed. Basically these would be similar to the preceding 1942 ships but before this was confirmed there was much debate behind the scenes. The new Mk VI gun turret was expected to be available in sufficient quantities to arm some of these ships and there was still a strong desire to see the design enlarged to enable an extra turret to be mounted aft. In addition a supply of Mk 37 directors was becoming available from the United States and this would be fitted with the new British Type 275 radar. However the final 1943 design retained the two Mk IV turrets fitted to the earlier 'Battles' although the new Mk 37 DCT would be fitted. In addition there would be an extra single 4.5in on the standard 55° Mk V mounting abaft the funnel.

It was anticipated that up to four flotillas (32 ships) of the design would be built under the 1943 and 1944 programmes and it was expected that changes in armament and layout would occur in the later ships. Thus it was proposed that the first 15 ships should carry the original Mk IV twin mounting followed by another six which would carry two of the new Mk VI mountings. A further five ships would be built to an enlarged design carrying three Mk VI mountings. However this plan was later modified and the 1943 programme was finalised as 24 ships which would all carry two Mk IV mountings except for the last two which would have the new Mk VI turrets. In addition an extra two ships were to be built to an expanded design with three Mk VI turrets, two forward and one aft. All these last four ships would dispense with the single 4.5in gun amidships.

On the standard vessels the close range AA armament would consist of two Mk 2 STAAG mountings aft, one Mk V twin 40mm amidships and two single 40mm in the bridge wings. In addition a total of 10 torpedo tubes in two Pentad mounts would be shipped and a Squid AS mortar was to be mounted on the quarterdeck. Radar outfit was similar to the earlier 'Battles'; type 293 at the foremast, Type 291 aft, Type 275 on the

DCT, Type 262 on the STAAGs and Type 282 on the STD for the Mk V mounting amidships.

Although all 24 ships of the 1943 programme were laid down between late 1943 and mid-1945, none was completed and only some had been launched by the end of hostilities in August 1945. It was obvious that the majority of them would not be required and on 25 September 1945 the Admiralty ordered the cessation of work on 16 of the ships of which seven had not been launched and were subsequently broken up on the slipway. The remainder were scrapped except for four (*Albuera, Jutland* (i), *Namur, Oudenarde*) which were moored up in various stages of completion with the possibility that they could be completed at a later date if required. A similar policy was adopted with other classes of ship, notably cruisers and aircraft carriers, and some of these were in fact

Below:
HMS *Barrosa* at Plymouth in 1949. The 4.5in gun amidships is clearly visible and she also carries a total of eight 40mm guns including two STAAG mountings aft. *Author's Collection*

Top right:
This shot of HMS *Aisne* shows the Mk 37 Director with the Type 275 twin radar antenna mounted on top. Note also the single 4.5in gun and the Mk V twin 40mm mounting amidships. *Skyfotos*

Above right:
The STAAG mountings on the after deckhouse are clearly visible in this view of HMS *Agincourt*. The ship wears the black funnel top which indicates that she is leader of the 4th Destroyer Squadron. Note that the single 4.5in gun is deactivated and cocooned. *Real Photos (2177)*

Right:
HMS *Agincourt* in 1966 following her conversion to an aircraft direction ship. The new mast, carrying the Type 965 and Type 293Q radars, is mounted on a very broad base. The fore part of the ship is unaltered except that the bridge structure has been enlarged on either side. *Skyfotos*

completed up to 15 years after the end of the war. However with the 1943 'Battles', although consideration was given in 1949-50 to completing some of the cancelled vessels, this was never done and the four ships concerned were eventually scrapped between 1950 and 1957.

This left a total of eight ships to be completed and work progressed at a much reduced rate so that the first to commission, *Dunkirk*, was not completed until November 1946 and the last, *Alamein*, until May 1948. The eight ships were destined to form the 4th Destroyer Flotilla, but by 1948 the postwar manning crisis had reached its height and so some were laid up leaving only *Agincourt*, *Aisne*, *Dunkirk* and *Jutland* in commission (the *Jutland* mentioned here was originally named *Malplaquet* and was renamed after launching. It should not be confused with the other *Jutland* mentioned in the preceding paragraph). *Matapan* went straight from her builders trials into reserve where she stayed until 1970!

The 4th Destroyer Flotilla/Squadron remained in existence until 1959 when *Alamein*, *Agincourt*, *Barrosa* and *Corruna* joined *Aisne* in reserve. In the meantime the 7th Destroyer Squadron had been formed in 1958 and consisted of *Dunkirk* and *Jutland* with the earlier 'Battle', HMS *Trafalgar*, as leader. These ships served until 1963, except for *Jutland* which paid off into reserve in 1961, and were the last operational 'Battle' class vessels in commission as conventional destroyers.

Top:
A stern view of *Aisne* showing the Seacat launcher and GWS21 director on the after deckhouse.
Wright and Logan

Right:
A close up of the short mainmast on *Agincourt*. At the top is various ESM gear while UHF and VHF communications aerials project to the left. On the right is the Type 277Q height finding radar.
C. & S. Taylor

Far right:
HMS *Barrosa* as converted. The single Squid AS mortar can be seen on the quarterdeck.
Imperial War Museum

As far back as 1944 it had been suggested that the later 'Battle' class ships could be fitted with a long-range air warning radar (at that time a Type 960) on a mast amidships at the expense of some of the torpedo tubes and close range AA armament. It was envisaged that these ships could then act as forward radar pickets for the fleet along the same lines as similarly equipped American destroyers, which had proved very useful in the Pacific, and would also be able to act as aircraft direction ships. At the time this idea was not carried forward as it was felt that such a conversion would detract from the ship's primary function as a destroyer. In fact this idea was obviously far ahead of its time as well as the Royal Navy was concerned, but in the postwar years a requirement was identified for a Fast Aircraft Detection Escort (FADE) which would accompany the fleet and provide facilities for the detection, identification and tracking of potential targets and be able to direct friendly aircraft to engage them. Consideration was given to building a new purpose-designed ship and also

o converting existing ships. The Type 62 conversion of the 'M' class destroyers has already been mentioned, but eventually the Type 61 frigate was ordered although this was too slow (24kt) to operate with a carrier task force. Initially it was expected that at least seven of these frigates would be built, but only four were completed and to make up the shortfall further consideration was given to the conversion of existing hulls. The latest long-range radar was the Type 965 which was available with two aerial outfits, AKE-1 and AKE-2. The latter was a massive double aerial weighing nearly 4 tons and could only be carried by a relatively large ship such as the 'Battle' class destroyer.

Various exercises throughout the 1950s confirmed the need for a fast aircraft direction ship but lack of suitable radar equipment delayed plans to convert destroyers to this role. Thus, although a decision in principle was made in 1955 to convert four of the 'Battle' class to aircraft direction ships, work did not begin until 1959. The four ships selected for conversion were *Agincourt*, *Aisne*, *Barrosa* and *Corunna* of which *Corunna* was the first to be completed in November 1962. The other three recommissioned the following year.

The alterations carried out were quite substantial. Forward, the main armament of four 4.5in guns was retained together with the Mk 37 director carrying Type 275 radar. Immediately abaft the bridge was a massive new lattice mast with its base straddling almost the whole width of the ship. This carried the AKE-2 aerial of the long range Type 965 radar while a Type 293Q cheese aerial was mounted below on a forward projecting platform.

All torpedo tubes and close range gun armament was removed and a series of deckhouses containing diesel generators and radar offices were erected abaft the funnel. A new lattice mainmast carried the parabolic aerial of the Type 277Q radar, which could be used as a height finder, and an impressive array of ESM and D/F aerials.

The original after deckhouse was extended and carried a GWS 21 Seacat guided weapon system for close range defence against air attack. This installation was the first operational deployment of Seacat, trials having previously been carried out aboard the destroyer *Decoy* in 1960 (qv). The missile director carried a Type 262 radar and was developed from the fire control equipment incorporated in the now obsolete STAAG mounting. Seacat was destined to become widely used aboard Royal Navy destroyers and frigates over the next 25 years, as well as being sold to many foreign navies. It was a simple robust missile and utilised a Command to Line of Sight (CLOS) guidance system. Originally it was intended that the aimer would track the target with a visual sight and, by means of a joystick control, send signals to the missile to direct it into the centre of his sight and thus on to the target. The use of the CRBFD with Type 262 radar allowed automatic tracking of the target and increased the system's effectiveness. The standard launcher carried four missiles and could be reloaded manually using spare missiles sent up from the magazine to the missile handling room on the after deckhouse.

The 'Battle' class aircraft direction conversions retained an AS capability with a single Squid mounted on the quarterdeck. Cost of the

conversions was quoted as around £2.25 million which was more than twice the original cost of the ships as completed. Despite this investment, their subsequent careers were relatively short.

On completion, *Corunna* and *Aisne* were allocated to the 7th Destroyer Squadron, while *Agincourt* and *Barrosa* joined the 5th and 8th respectively. These arrangements were short-lived as by 1963 the Royal Navy's frigate and destroyer squadrons were reorganised into escort squadrons made up of a mixture of various types so as to provide an increased overall capability in each group of ships. *Corruna* subsequently started a refit in 1965 but was then laid up in reserve where she remained until being scrapped in 1975.

Aisne spent most of her time in the Far East, serving with the 23rd and 30th Escort Squadron before a final deployment to the West Indies in 1967-68. She then paid off into reserve and was scrapped in 1970. *Agincourt* remained in Home and Mediterranean waters but her short career ended in 1966 when she went into reserve. *Barrosa* was mostly in the Far East before paying off at the end of 1968, although she was not finally scrapped for another 10 years.

The somewhat premature retirement of these ships was mainly due to the policies of the Labour Government which came to power in 1964. It was committed to a withdrawal of British Forces from the Far East, with a parallel reduction in the size of the fleet. A decision in the late 1960s to run down the carrier force also meant that the requirement for aircraft direction ships was reduced. Finally, the emergence of the new general purpose frigates such as the 'Tribal' and 'Leander' classes, which carried the Type 965 radar and incorporated up to date operations rooms, meant that they could replace the destroyer conversions in most circumstances.

However, the story of the Royal Navy 'Battle' classes was not quite at an end. As the last operational ships were being laid up in reserve, another ship of the class was being reactivated. This was HMS *Matapan* which had been laid up on completion in 1947 having carried out only 150hr steaming whilst on her trials. After 21 years she was selected for use as a sonar trials ship in a programme funded by both the RN and USN. Work on the conversion for her new role began at Portsmouth in February 1971 and she recommissioned two years later.

As a non-operational ship she was stripped of all armament and the forecastle deck was extended right aft to the stern in order to provide increased internal volume for the accommodation of personnel and equipment during the trials. A new enclosed bridge was fitted and a plated foremast carried a navigation radar and communications aerials. A second funnel was erected aft, but this housed the exhausts for the diesel generators installed to power the sonars, and a helicopter landing deck was also erected aft. The ship did not carry her own helicopter but the landing deck was used for ferrying men and supplies from ashore as required. The lines of the bow were considerably altered with increased rake and flare while below the waterline a large bulbous bow housed the transducer array for the sonar. The trials programme lasted for nearly five years and the ship was finally laid up in 1978 and scrapped the following year.

The Australian 'Battle' Class Destroyers — *Anzac, Tobruk*

It will be remembered that the wartime programme for the 'Battle' class flotillas included provision for later ships to be armed with the new Mk VI turret, but these were cancelled at the end of the war. However, in 1945 the RAN had ordered two ships of this type to be built in Australian yards. Despite the end of hostilities, the orders were not cancelled and both ships were laid down in 1946 although progress was slow and *Tobruk* was not completed until 1950, with her sister ship taking another year.

As completed these ships differed in some detail from their Royal Navy counterparts. The higher

Below:
HMAS *Anzac* as completed with three STAAG mountings aft and a distinctive cowl atop the funnel. Unlike the later British 'Battles', she is equipped with a Mk VI director. *Imperial War Museum*

profile of the Mk VI turret meant that the bridge was slightly raised to retain adequate forward visibility. The higher rate of fire of the 4.5in guns meant that the single 4.5in gun abaft the funnel was not required and the weight saved by its removal meant that a third STAAG mounting could be carried instead. Another six 40mm guns in single mountings were also carried. Other armament consisted of 10 torpedo tubes (two Pentad) and a Squid AS mortar aft. A distinctive funnel cowl was carried by both ships.

Tobruk remained in service until 1960 when she was placed in reserve, but *Anzac* continued as a fleet training ship with the STAAG mountings and torpedo tubes removed. In 1966 she was further modified for this role with B turret removed and replaced by a deckhouse, while a further deckhouse was erected aft. She was laid up and listed for disposal in 1974.

Name	No	Laid Down	Launched	Completed	Builder	Yard	Remarks	
Armada	D14	29/12/42	09/12/43	02/07/45	Hawthorn Leslie	Hebburn	Arr Inverkeithing for scrap	12/11/65
Barfleur	D80	28/11/42	01/11/43	14/09/44	Swan Hunter	Tyne	Arr Dalmuir for scrap	29/09/66
Cadiz	D79	10/05/43	16/09/44	12/04/46	Fairfield	Govan	PN 1957. Sunk Indo-Pakistan War	1971
Camperdown	D32	30/11/42	08/02/44	18/06/45	Fairfield	Govan	Arr Faslane for scrap	09/70
Finisterre	D55	08/12/42	22/06/44	11/09/45	Fairfield	Govan	Arr Dalmuir for scrap	12/06/67
Gabbard	D47	02/02/44	16/03/45	10/12/46	Swan Hunter	Tyne	PN 1957. In service	1987
Gravelines	D24	10/08/43	30/11/44	14/06/46	Cammell Laird	Birkenhead	Arr Rosyth for scrap	04/04/61
Hogue	D74	06/01/43	21/04/44	24/07/45	Cammell Laird	Birkenhead	Singapore for scrap	07/03/62
Lagos	D44	08/05/43	04/05/44	02/11/45	Cammell Laird	Birkenhead	Arr Bo'ness for scrap	06/67
St James	D65	20/05/43	07/06/45	12/07/46	Fairfield	Govan	Arr Newport for scrap	19/03/61
St Kitts	D18	08/09/43	04/10/44	21/01/46	Swan Hunter	Tyne	Arr Sunderland for scrap	19/02/62
Saintes	D84	08/06/43	19/07/44	27/09/46	Hawthorn Leslie	Hebburn	Arr Cairn Ryan for scrap	01/09/72
Sluys	D60	24/11/43	28/02/45	30/09/46	Cammell Laird	Birkenhead	I.R.N. 1966. Still extant	1987
Solebay	D70	03/02/43	22/02/44	11/10/45	Hawthorn Leslie	Hebburn	Arr Troon for scrapping	11/08/67
Trafalgar	D77	15/02/43	12/01/44	23/07/45	Swan Hunter	Wallsend	Scrapped	1970
Vigo	D231	11/09/43	27/09/45	09/12/46	Fairfield	Govan	Arr Faslane for scrap	06/12/64
Agincourt	D86	12/12/43	29/01/45	25/06/47	Hawthorn Leslie	Hebburn	Arr Sunderland for scrap	27/10/74
Aisne	D22	26/08/43	12/05/45	20/03/47	Vickers Armstrong	Tyne	Arr Inverkeithing for scrap	27/06/70
Alamein	D17	01/03/44	28/05/45	21/05/48	Hawthorn Leslie	Hebburn	Arr Blyth for scrapping	01/12/64
Barrosa	D68	28/12/43	17/01/45	14/02/47	J. Brown	Clyde	Arr Blyth for scrapping	01/12/78
Corunna	D97	12/04/44	29/05/45	06/06/47	Swan Hunter	Wallsend	Arr Blyth for scrapping	11/09/75
Dunkirk	D09	19/07/44	27/08/45	27/11/46	Alex Stephen	Linthouse	Arr Faslane for scrapping	22/11/65
Jutland(ii)	D62	27/11/44	20/02/46	30/04/47	Alex Stephens	Linthouse	Arr Blyth for scrapping	14/05/65
Matapan	D43	11/03/44	30/04/45	05/09/47	J. Brown	Clydebank	Arr Blyth for scrapping	11/08/79
Anzac	D59	23/09/46	20/08/48	22/03/51	HMA Dockyard	Williamstown	RAN. Scrapped	1975
Tobruk	D37	05/08/46	20/12/47	08/05/50	Cockatoo	Sydney	RAN. Scrapped	1975

Data:	1942 'Battle' class, HMS *Lagos* (1946)	**Data:**	'Battle' class AD Con, HMS *Aisne* (1946)
Displacement (tons):	2,315 standard, 3,290 full load	**Displacement** (tons):	2,480 standard, 3,430 full load
Length/Beam (ft):	379 (oa)/40.25	**Length/Beam** (ft):	379 (oa)/40.5
Draught (ft):	13 (light), 15.25 (full load)	**Draught** (ft):	17.5 (full load)
Armament:	4×4.5in on 2×Mk IV twin mountings, 1×4in Mk XXIII, 4×Mk IV Hazemeyer twin 40mm, 4×single 40mm, 2×single 2pdr, 8×21in torpedo tubes, depth charges	**Armament:**	4×4.5in on 2×Mk IV twin mountings, 1×GWS 21 Seacat AA missile system, 2×Squid AS mortars
Radars:	Types 293, 291, 275, 282	**Radars:**	Types 965, 277Q, 293Q, 275, 262
Machinery:	2×Admiralty 3-drum boilers (400lb/sq in/700°F), 2×shafts, Parsons geared turbines, 50,000shp	**Machinery:**	As 1942 'Battle' class
Speed/Range:	31kt/4,400nm @ 20kt	**Speed/Range:**	31kt/3,000nm @ 20kt
Oil Fuel (tons):	766	**Oil Fuel** (tons):	680
Complement:	247	**Complement:**	268

'Weapon' Class Destroyers — *Battleaxe, Broadsword, Crossbow, Scorpion*

While the 'Battle' class building programme got underway in 1943 and kept the larger yards fully employed for the remainder of the war, most of the smaller yards were building the Emergency War Programme destroyers of the 'S/Z' and 'C' classes. As these yards would not be capable of accommodating the 'Battle' class, a smaller design was drawn up to follow on from the 'C' classes. Design work started in 1942 from the basis that overall dimensions would be similar to the preceding 'S' to 'C' classes but the final specification incorporated two major changes from previous practice which totally altered the appearance of the new ships which were to be named after various weapons.

The first change concerned the main armament and again reflected the high priority given to defence against air attack, and in a reversal of previous policy the 4in HA gun was accepted from the outset as the main armament of a fleet destroyer. Admittedly some of the wartime 'L', 'O' and 'P' classes had been built with this type of gun but this was mainly due to supply difficulties with the 4.7in originally specified. The 'Weapon' class would carry six 4in, in three Mk XIX twin mountings — two forward and one aft — together with a Mk VI director with Type 275 radar. Close range AA fire would be provided by two STAAG mountings winged out on the after deckhouse, and two twin 20mm power mountings in the bridge

Top:
HMS *Broadsword* as completed in 1948 with 4in guns fore and aft and the twin Squids before the bridge. *Yarrow*

Above:
The Squid mortars in front of the bridge are clearly visible in this aerial view of HMS *Battleaxe*, as are the two Pentad torpedo mountings fore and aft of the black topped funnel. *Skyfotos*

Bottom:
Scorpion and *Crossbow* were completed with both 4in mountings before the bridge. This view of *Scorpion* emphasises the awkward lines of these ships with the fore funnel shrouded in the foremast. *Skyfotos*

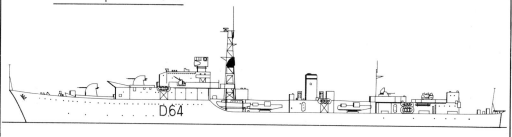

HMS SCORPION

Weapon Class Destroyer

As Completed 1947

D.64

BUILDERS – J. Samuel White and Co. Ltd.

LAID DOWN – 16th DEC 1944

LAUNCHED – 15th AUG 1946

COMPLETED – 17th SEP 1947

LENGTH – 365 ft.

BEAM – 38 ft.

DRAUGHT – 14 ft.

SPEED – 32.5 knots.

Left:
In 1954 *Scorpion* was fitted with a Mk 10 Limbo AS mortar instead of the two Squids. Its three barrels can be seen pointing skywards abaft the two STAAG mountings on the after deckhouse.
Wright and Logan

Bottom left:
As converted to an aircraft direction ship, HMS *Broadsword* carries a Type 965 radar with an AKE-1 aerial. An MRS 8 Director has replaced the Mk VI director above the bridge.
Imperial War Museum

wings. Two sets of quadruple torpedo tubes completed the armament but AS capability could be improved by removing one set of tubes to increase depth charge capacity or both sets to enable two AS mortars to be carried. At one stage it was suggested that one of the 4in mountings be removed to allow two Squid mortars to be mounted instead and this would have allowed retention of the torpedoes (at an early stage consideration was given to having fixed torpedo tubes mounted in the bow, rather like MTBs, but this idea was short lived).

The other major change was in the layout of the propulsion machinery. Standard layout in British destroyers since the inception of the 'J' class had been to concentrate the boilers together so that a single funnel would suffice and the engine rooms were immediately aft. This arrangement was adopted to reduce hull length and give the clearest possible arcs of fire for the light AA armament. However, the major disadvantage was that a single hit from a torpedo or heavy shell could put the machinery out of action. This was, at the time, considered an acceptable risk but war experience suggested that a unit arrangement for the machinery would offer a greater chance of survival despite the associated penalties of increased weight and length. In fact, compared to the 'S' class, the 'Weapons' were only a few feet longer (although displacement increased by over 200 tons) and the unit arrangement was standard on American destroyers. Working aft, the machinery spaces in the 'Weapon' class consisted of a boiler room, engine room, oil compartment, engine room and boiler room. Externally the result was two widely spaced funnels but, in order to give clear fields of fire, these were kept as small as possible. In a unique arrangement, the fore funnel was shrouded within the lattice foremast with a curved cowl to deflect the hot gases aft, while the thin, straight, second funnel stood amidships. It has to be said that the end result was one of the oddest designs ever to join the Royal Navy and they were also criticised on the grounds that they were undergunned. Nevertheless, their AA capability was far superior to that of the Emergency

Programme destroyers and they were intended to be functional rather than beautiful.

In April 1943 orders for two flotillas (16 ships) were placed with various yards including five from J. S. White at Cowes. The latter would be all-welded while the rest would use a mixture of welded and riveted construction. A further four ships were ordered the following month and construction began in 1944. However, by December of that year it was apparent that the end of the war was in sight and so three ships (*Grenade*, *Halberd*, *Poinard*) were cancelled at that stage. With the end of hostilities in August 1945, cancellations of 10 orders were issued in September and October. In January 1946 further instructions were given that *Rifle* was to be broken up on the slipway while *Cutlass* and *Culverin* would be launched and then broken up.

These cancellations left only four ships still building. *Battleaxe* and *Crossbow* had already been launched and *Broadsword* and *Scorpion* followed in February and August 1946. *Scorpion*, by this stage, had already been renamed twice. Originally she was ordered as HMS *Centaur* and would have been one of the fifth flotilla of 'C' class destroyers, but when these were cancelled and the contract was reissued for a 'Weapon' class she was renamed *Tomahawk*. However, after the war the First Sea Lord, Admiral of the Fleet Viscount Cunningham, expressed regret that there was no ship named *Scorpion* in the fleet (an earlier ship of this name had been the Admiral's first destroyer command). When somebody on the Ships Names Committee discovered that a Scorpion was a form of medieval catapult the problem was solved and *Tomahawk* was again renamed.

The four ships were actually completed to a revised design. When laid down it was anticipated that they would be operating in the Pacific where air attack was a much greater threat than the much reduced Japanese submarine fleet. However, in the era following 1945 the submarine threat was again addressed and it was decided that the 'Weapons' would be completed as fleet escorts with two Squid mortars replacing one of the 4in mountings (B gun in *Battleaxe* and *Broadsword* and X gun in the others). To offset the loss of one twin 4in mounting, torpedo armament was increased to 10 tubes in two Pentad mounts and the final AA disposition was two STAAGs supplemented by single 40mm guns in the bridge wings instead of the original 20mm.

Radar was the standard destroyer outfit consisting of Type 293M at the top of the lattice foremast, Type 275 and 262 gunnery radars, and a Type 291 air warning on a pole mainmast. In addition VHF and UHF D/F were fitted as well as IFF equipment. *Scorpion* carried Type 160X sonar while the others carried the Type 144/147 combination which was normal for Squid-equipped ships.

All four ships were plagued with turbine troubles when they first entered service, mainly due to faults in the design and casting of the casings. The astern turbine casing caused problems and these were remedied by blanking off the steam feed to the lower half of the casing which reduced astern power. The ships were among the first to be fitted with a device called 'Nightshirt' which was intended to reduce propeller cavitation noise by generating a stream of bubbles from a lattice web situated in front of the propellers. Although this system was effective in reducing noise, it did not prove to be very robust and was eventually removed.

The 'Weapon' class destroyers formed the 6th Destroyer Flotilla/Squadron with the Home Fleet,

operating together until 1953 when *Broadsword* went into reserve, followed by *Crossbow* in 1955 — their places being taken by two 'Co' class destroyers. All except *Broadsword* appeared at the 1953 Coronation Review.

In 1954 *Scorpion* was fitted with a Mk 10 Limbo AS mortar instead of the two Squids as a trial.

Below:
A close-up view of the new mast and AKE-1 aerial aboard HMS *Battleaxe*. The foremast carries a Type 293Q and various ESM equipment.
C. & S. Taylor

Bottom:
HMS *Crossbow* in 1959 while serving with the 2nd Destroyer Squadron after conversion. Note the extra deckhouses filling the spaces left by the removal of the torpedo armament. *Wright and Logan*

installation pending modernisation of the whole class. A programme for all four was proposed in 1953 which entailed the fitting of Limbo with Types 170, 184 and 162 sonars, two twin L70 Bofors with a CRBFD replacing the STAAG mountings, one set of torpedo tubes removed and a new MRS3 director replacing the Mk VI above the bridge. In the event, no interim modernisations were carried out and all four ships were laid up in reserve by 1956. In fact the 'Weapon' class as originally completed could be considered as the Royal Navy's first modern fast fleet escort with an all-round anti-aircraft and anti-submarine capability. In retrospect they may be considered as fast frigates rather than as destroyers despite their ancestry.

Mention has already been made of the requirement for aircraft direction ships in the postwar era. Initially the 'Weapons' were excluded from consideration for conversion in view of their proposed ASW modernisation. When this was cancelled they were made available for conversion as interim aircraft direction ships pending the completion of the 'Battle' class conversions. The work, which was not as extensive as the later programmes, entailed the removal of the torpedo tubes so that additional deckhouses could be substituted and the provision of a new lattice mast stepped between the funnels to carry a single element AKE-1 aerial for a Type 965 radar. Gun armament remained as before but the Mk VI director was replaced by a new MRS 8 director with Type 262R radar. In addition, Battleaxe and Broadsword had their Squids transposed aft and the after 4in mounting brought forward so that all four ships now carried their main armament before the bridge. A notable omission was the lack of a height-finding radar but this was probably precluded by topweight considerations.

After conversion, Broadsword served with the 7th DS at home and in the Mediterranean until 1963 when she was laid up in reserve. Crossbow and Battleaxe served with the 'Daring' class destroyers of the 2nd and 5th DS until Battleaxe was severely damaged in a collision with the frigate Ursa in the Firth of Clyde in August 1962. The destroyer's hull was split vertically down to the keel and the damage was so bad that she had to be scrapped. It was claimed that a contributory factor in this incident was the lack of astern power in these ships due to the modifications described earlier in this section.

Crossbow remained in commission until the following January when she was also laid up. Scorpion, still the odd man out with her Limbo mortar, had a similar career to Broadsword until paying off in April 1963. By this time all four 'Battle' class conversions were in service and the 'Weapons' were surplus to requirements. Between 1967 and 1970 Crossbow served as a static harbour training ship for HMS Sultan and was later scrapped in 1972. Scorpion and Broadsword were used in underwater explosion trials before being scrapped in 1971 and 1968 respectively.

The 'Weapon' class were something of an aberration in British destroyer design and were often criticised as being underarmed and difficult to handle. However, they represented the first attempt in the postwar era to produce a ship capable of meeting the new range of threats posed by faster aircraft and submarines. Their admitted failure was due as much to the lack of suitable weapons and equipment as it was to design philosophy.

Name	No	Laid Down	Launched	Completed	Builder	Yard	Remarks	
Battleaxe	D118	22/04/44	12/06/45	23/10/47	Yarrow	Clyde	Arr Blyth for scrapping	20/10/64
Broadsword	D31	20/07/44	05/02/46	04/10/48	Yarrow	Scotstoun	Arr Inverkeithing for scrap	08/10/68
Crossbow	D96	26/08/44	20/12/45	04/03/48	Thornycroft	Woolston	Arr Briton Ferry for scrap	21/01/72
Scorpion	D64	16/12/44	15/08/46	17/09/47	J. S. White	Cowes	Scrapped Bo'ness	1971

Data: 'Weapon' class, HMS Battleaxe (1950)

Displacement (tons):	1,980 standard, 2,825 full load
Length/Beam (ft):	365 (oa)/38
Draught (ft):	12 (light), 14.5 (full load)
Armament:	4×4in DP on 2×Mk XIX mountings, 2×STAAG twin 40mm, 2×single 40mm, 10×21in torpedo tubes, 2×Squid AS mortars
Radars:	Types 293, 291, 275, 282
Machinery:	2×Foster Wheeler boilers (430lb/sq in/750°F), 2×shafts, Parsons geared turbines, 40,000shp
Speed/Range:	31kt/5,000nm @ 20kt
Oil Fuel (tons):	630
Complement:	254

Data: 'Weapon' class AD Con, HMS Scorpion (1961)

Displacement (tons):	2,280 standard, 2,935 full load
Length/Beam (ft):	As built
Draught (ft):	17 (full load)
Armament:	4×4in DP on 2×Mk XIX mountings, 2×STAAG twin 40mm mountings, 1×Mk 10 Limbo AS mortar
Radars:	Types 965 (AKE-1), 293Q, 262/262R
Machinery:	As Battleaxe
Speed/Range:	31kt/5,000nm @ 15kt
Oil Fuel (tons):	630
Complement:	234

'Daring' Class Destroyers — *Daring, Dainty, Decoy, Defender, Delight, Diamond, Diana, Duchess*

The 'Daring' class were the largest conventional destroyers built by the Royal Navy and represented the sum total of wartime experience. A total of 16 ships was originally authorised under the 1944 building programme and orders were placed early in 1945, although none had been laid down by the end of the war. In December 1945, when work had commenced on only two ships, half of the orders were cancelled, leaving eight ships to be completed. However, the construction programme was a long drawn out affair and the last two of the class were not laid down until as late as 1949. All eight entered service between 1952 and 1954.

Originally the 'Darings' were intended to be a continuation of the 'Battle' class, slightly enlarged to carry three Mk VI twin 4.5in gun turrets. However, the design was recast during 1944 to incorporate new high pressure steam machinery which utilised double-reduction gearing for increased efficiency. Compared to the 'Battle' class, power output was raised from 50,000 to 54,000shp and the boilers produced steam at an operating pressure increased from 400 to 650lb/sq in. A unit arrangement of the machinery, as in the 'Weapon' class, resulted in a similar ungainly arrangement of two funnels with the forward one enclosed within the lattice mast.

Hull dimensions were increased, in particular the beam which was now 43ft. Construction was intended to be all-welded but composite construction was adopted for *Daring, Decoy* and *Diana* as the yards concerned did not have the necessary welding facilities. Aluminium was used for some of the internal bulkheads (one of the first uses of this material in Royal Navy ships) and ⅜in protective plating was provided for the turrets and bridge structure. More armour protected the cable runs for the fire control system. The forward superstructure was a large and imposing block housing an enlarged operations room surmounted by an open bridge with sloping faces to the sides.

The main armament (three Mk VI twin 4.5in mountings) was to be controlled by a Mk VI director with Type 275 radar while a MRS1 barrage director was to be carried aft to provide local control for the after turret. Other planned armament comprised three STAAG twin 40mm mountings — two abreast the foremast and the other on the centreline aft — 10 21in torpedo tubes in two Pentad mounts and four depth charge throwers with provision for 70 DCs. After the war this arrangement was slightly modified and the ships were completed with a Mk V Utility twin 40mm mounting instead of the after STAAG, a CRBFD instead of the MRS1 and a Squid A/S mortar instead of the depth charges.

As completed, the radar outfit consisted of a Type 293Q combined air/surface warning at the top of the lattice foremast with a Type 974 navigation radar below, a Type 291 on the pole mainmast and Type 275 and 262 gunnery radars. FH4 VHF/DF was fitted atop the foremast and a number of whip aerials for communications sprouted from the bridge, after funnel and superstructure.

The result of all these modifications and alterations was a ship of 2,950 tons standard displacement compared to the 2,550 tons of the 'Battle' class and 1,870 tons of the later 'C' group destroyers. When they entered service in the early 1950s, having cost an average of £2.5 million each, the Admiralty considered that they were something more than mere destroyers and almost the equivalent of a light cruiser. Consequently, for a while, they were not classified as destroyers but were referred to as 'Daring Class' ships. In fact they were only slightly larger than the American 'Gearing' class destroyers completed between 1944 and 1947 and much smaller than the four 'Mitscher' class destroyers laid down for the USN in 1949 which displaced 3,675 tons (standard). It was certainly true that the 'Darings' represented a significant increase in capability compared with the earlier Royal Navy destroyers but they only reflected the wartime trend for increased size made necessary by the new development in weapons and equipment, and the increase in manning complements to operate them. The result was a ship which was expensive to build and which could no longer be considered as expendable as the prewar standard fleet destroyer.

One variation of equipment fitted to the eight 'Daring' class ships meant that they were

Top right:
A fine view of HMS *Duchess* as completed in 1952. Note the angled faces of the bridge and the STAAG mounting abreast the foremast. *Vosper Thornycroft*

Above right:
The difference in size between HMS *Delight* and the 'Weapon' class destroyer *Battleaxe* is clearly shown in this bow view of the two ships. The 'Darings' had a beam of 43ft compared with 38ft for the 'Weapon' class. *Imperial War Museum*

Right:
This beam view of HMS *Decoy* illustrates the unusual funnel arrangement of these ships. Note the high angle of elevation of the guns in B turret. *Real Photos (S2172)*

effectively split into two groups of four ships for most of their careers. *Daring, Dainty, Defender* and *Delight* had a dc electrical installation while the other four had a more modern ac system. The dc group were deployed to the Mediterranean on completion while the other four joined the Home Fleet. These groups were initially unnamed due to the official 'Daring Class' status of the ships, but eventually they became the 2nd and 5th Destroyer Squadrons respectively, each group rotating between the Mediterranean and home waters at regular intervals. During this time *Diamond, Defender, Decoy* and *Duchess* appeared at the 1953 Coronation Review and in 1956 *Diamond, Defender, Daring, Diana* and *Duchess* took part in support of the Suez operation.

In 1958 the dc group paid off for refitting during which the after torpedo tubes were removed and replaced by a deckhouse giving much needed extra accommodation space. Subsequent to this, the four ships served at home and in the Mediterranean until going into reserve in 1961.

Between 1962 and 1964 the four dc ships underwent a further modernisation when the remaining set of torpedo tubes was removed and replaced by another deckhouse so that there was a continuous run of superstructure aft of the foremast. The two STAAG mountings were replaced by Mk V utility twin 40mm mountings with their associated STDs while the original Mk VI director was replaced by a lightweight MRS3 director incorporating a new Type 903 gunnery radar which featured automatic target tracking.

Above left:
In an effort to improve appearance some ships were fitted with a raked casing for the second funnel as seen in this view of HMS *Diana*. This modification was not long-lived and was later removed.
Real Photos (2176)

Left:
Contemporary with the 'Darings' were the 'Holland' class destroyers of the Netherlands Navy. With a standard displacement of 2,164 tons, they were smaller than the 'Darings' and carried only four 4.7in guns in two twin turrets, a single 40mm gun and no torpedoes. However they were handsome ships and the Swedish-designed 4.7in guns and turrets were generally considered to be better than the British 4.5in Mk VI turret. *Real Photos (S3456)*

Above:
HMS *Defender*, seen here following a refit in 1965. The light AA armament now comprised three Mk V twin 40mm mountings and the Mk VI director has been replaced by an MRS 3 with a Type 903 radar. All torpedoes have been removed. *Royal Navy*

The subsequent career of these four ships was limited as they were shared between various escort squadrons, although for the first time they were deployed east of Suez. However, *Delight* paid off into reserve for the last time in 1967 and was

followed over the next two years by *Dainty*, *Defender* and *Daring* as part of the general reduction in destroyer numbers caused by the political decision to withdraw from the Far East and Indian Ocean areas.

The four ac ships, forming the 5th DS, were also modernised during 1959-60. As with the other ships, the after torpedo tubes were removed and replaced by a new deckhouse. In addition, the STAAG mountings were removed and, in this instance, replaced by single 40mm guns and the Mk VI director replaced by the new MRS3 with the Type 903 radar. The apparent reduction in the close range anti-aircraft armament was in preparation for the installation of the Seacat surface-to-air guided missile. *Decoy* was modified during the refit to act as a trials ship for the new missile and the after Mk V Bofors mounting was removed and replaced by a quadruple Seacat launcher while the CRBFD was modified so that it could be used for tracking and controlling the missile. In addition the STAAG mountings were removed and replaced by single 40mm guns. The trials were very successful and resulted in the widespread use of the Seacat aboard RN ships. It was planned that all 'Daring' class ships would eventually be fitted with the missile, but the fact that this was never done was an indication of the fact that these ships were

lready regarded as obsolescent at this time. Decoy's Seacat installation was removed after the trials were completed in October 1962.

Following this modernisation, *Duchess, Diana* and *Diamond* joined the 5th DS for a short period before being reallocated to the new escort groups in 1963. In 1964 *Duchess* was transferred to the RAN as a replacement for HMAS *Voyager* which was lost that year. Originally this was intended to be for a four-year period, but the loan was extended to 1972 when the ship was purchased by the RAN and underwent conversion to a training ship to replace the 'Battle' class destroyer *Anzac*. This entailed the removal of the remaining torpedo tubes, the after 4.5in turret and the Squid AS mortar. A large deckhouse was erected aft for use as classrooms and the after funnel was given a streamlined casing. The ship remained in service

until 1977 when she was laid up; she was subsequently scrapped in 1980.

Decoy, Diana and *Diamond* paid off in 1969-70, although the latter was used for many years as a static harbour training ship at Portsmouth until finally scrapped in 1981. The other two were sold to Peru and underwent an extensive refit by Cammell Laird at Birkenhead before recommissioning with their new owners in 1973. *Decoy* was renamed *Ferre* while *Diana* became *Palacios*. The modernisation of these ships resulted in some improvement to their appearance as the lattice foremast was replaced by a plated structure completely enclosing the fore funnel and a raked cowl was fitted to the after funnel. The forward torpedo tubes were retained but the space between the after funnel and X turret was cleared to leave room for eight fixed Exocet surface-to-surface missile launchers. Light AA armament consisted of two single 40mm guns in the bridge wings while the Squid mortar was retained aft. A new radar outfit, including a Plessey AWS-1, and a modernised fire control system were also fitted. In 1977-78 *Palacios* was further modified by the removal of the after 4.5in mounting, two Exocet launchers and the Squid to make room for a helicopter landing deck. A hangar was also erected initially, but this was later removed. The single 40mm guns were replaced by Breda twin 40mm mountings with a very high rate of fire and the after funnel was given a streamlined casing — a modification which all owners of the ex-RN ships seem unable to resist! *Ferre* was also modernised but still retains all three 4.5in mountings although the number of Exocet launchers has also been reduced to six. Both ships were in service as late as 1985.

Name	No	Laid Down	Launched	Completed	Builder	Yard	Remarks	
Daring	D05	29/09/45	10/08/49	08/03/52	Swan Hunter	Tyne	Arr Blyth for scrap	15/06/7[
Dainty	D108	17/12/45	16/08/50	26/02/53	J. S. White	Cowes	Scrapped Cairnryan	02/70
Decoy	D106	22/09/46	29/03/49	28/04/53	Yarrow	Scotstoun	Peruvian Navy 1969. In service	1987
Defender	D114	22/03/49	27/07/50	05/12/52	Alex Stephens	Linthouse	Scrapped Inverkeithing	1972
Delight	D119	05/09/46	21/12/50	09/10/53	Fairfield	Govan	Scrapped Inverkeithing	1971
Diamond	D35	15/03/49	14/06/50	21/02/52	J. Brown	Clydebank	Scrapped Medway	1981
Diana	D126	03/04/47	08/05/52	19/03/54	Yarrow	Scotstoun	Peruvian Navy 1969. In service	1987
Duchess	D154	02/07/48	09/04/51	23/10/52	Thornycroft	Woolston	RAN 1964. Towed for scrap	09/07/8(
Vampire	D11	01/07/52	27/10/56	23/06/59	Cockatoo	Sydney	RAN.	13/08/87
Vendetta	D08	04/07/59	03/05/54	26/11/58	HMA Dockyard	Williamstown	RAN. Decommissioned	28/06/79
Voyager	D04	10/10/49	01/05/52	12/02/58	Cockatoo	Sydney	RAN. Collided HMAS *Melbourne*	11/02/64

Data: 'Daring' class, HMS *Dainty* (1960)

Displacement (tons): 2,950 standard, 3,580 full load

Length/Beam (ft): 390 (oa)/43

Draught (ft): 17 (full load)

Armament: 6×4.5in on 3×Mk VI twin turrets, 2×STAAG twin 40mm mountings, 1×Mk V twin 40mm, 5×21in torpedo tubes, 1×Squid AS mortar

Radars: Types 293Q, 275, 262

Machinery: 2×Foster Wheeler boilers (650lb/sq in/850°F), 2×shafts, Parsons geared turbines, 54,000shp

Speed/Range: 32kt/4,400nm @ 20kt

Oil Fuel (tons): 618

Complement: 286

The Australian 'Daring' Class Destroyers — *Vampire, Vendetta, Voyager*

As the Australian Navy had been involved in the later part of the 'Battle' class programme, it was a natural step for them to order four of the subsequent 'Daring' class in 1946. However, construction proceeded at an even slower rate than the Royal Navy vessels as the first pair were not laid down until 1949 and were only completed in 1958. The second pair were laid down in 1952 but one of these (*Waterhen*) was cancelled and scrapped on the slipway in 1954 while the other did not commission until as late as 1959.

The Australian vessels were completed to a standard similar to that of the RN ships after modernisations in the late 1950s. They carried only one set of torpedo tubes and the after deckhouse was extended to fill in the gap. Light AA armament consisted of two Mk V twin 40mm mountings abaft the second funnel and two single 40mm guns abreast the foremast, while two CRBFD were carried fore and aft of the after funnel. A Mk 10 Limbo replaced the Squid on the quarterdeck. The radar outfit was similar to the RN ships except that the obsolete Type 291 was deleted.

On entering service the three ships formed the 10th Destroyer Squadron of the RAN. *Voyager* had the shortest career which ended when she sank following a collision with the aircraft carrier HMS *Melbourne* during exercises on 11 February 1964. As related, her loss was offset by the loan of the destroyer *Duchess* from the Royal Navy.

Between 1970 and 1973, *Vampire* and *Vendetta* underwent a substantial modernisation programme which resulted in a considerable change in their appearance. The lattice foremast was dismantled which meant that the fore funnel coul[now be plainly seen, and both funnels wer[increased in height and given new tapering casing[with prominent curved cowls on the top. A shor[lattice mast structure was erected abaft the bridg[and this carried a Dutch WM22 fire control rada[housed in a spherical weatherproof dome, whil[the bridge itself was now totally enclosed. Th[remaining torpedo tubes were removed and [Philips LW-02 long range radar was mounted on [plated mast in front of the after funnel with [further fire control radar abaft the funnel. The gu[armament (six 4.5in and six 40mm guns) remaine[unchanged.

Both ships recommissioned to form the new 2nd Destroyer Squadron and served until *Ven detta* was laid up in 1979. The following yea[*Vampire* was modified to act as a training ship b[the removal of the twin 40mm mountings and the[Limbo mortar, and continued in that role unti[laid up.

The modernisations carried out to the 'Daring[class ships by the Peruvian and Australian navie[show the potential for extending the life o[warships. Since 1945 the Royal Navy has preferre[to sell off old ships and build new replacements bu[in recent years this policy has led to a marke[decrease in the numbers of ships available. Had i[not been for the policy of the British Governmen[in the 1960s to reduce the size and role of the[Royal Navy, it is possible that some of the RN['Darings' might have been kept on and modern[ised. If nothing else, their main armament would[have provided useful support for amphibiou[operations.

94

Above:
The Australian 'Darings' differed from their British counterparts in the distribution and composition of the light AA armament, mounting only one set of

torpedo tubes, having two CRBF Directors fore and aft of the second funnel, and a Limbo aft instead of a Squid. This is HMAS *Vendetta.*
Imperial War Museum

'G' Class Destroyers

Although the 'Darings' were the last conventional destroyers to be built for the Royal Navy, they were not quite the last to be designed. As with the earlier 'Battle' class, the size of the new ships meant that some yards could not be utilised for their construction and so a parallel but smaller design was also produced for construction under the 1944 programme. Designated the 'G' class, these ships would have been similar in profile to the 'Weapon' class but the beam was increased so that the main armament would consist of two twin 4.5in Mk VI mountings as fitted to the 'Darings'. A flotilla of eight ships was ordered in 1944 but none had been laid down when hostilities ended in August 1945 and all were cancelled in the following December. Like the 'Weapon' class, a number of alternative armament layouts were considered including an enhanced light AA battery or the mounting of two Squid mortars, both of these necessitating the removal of the torpedo tubes.

Although not built, the 'G' class design formed the basis of a number of destroyer projects in the early postwar period. However, the idea of further

conventional destroyers faded in the late 1940s as the potential impact of new weapon systems, particularly guided missiles, on warship designs was fully realised. The next chapter will see the birth of a completely new type of ship to carry on the destroyer tradition.

Data:	Projected 'G' class, HMS *Gael* (1945)
Displacement (tons):	2,200 standard, 3,000 full load
Length/Beam (ft):	365 (oa)/39.5
Draught (ft):	10 (light), 12.5 (full load)
Armament:	4×4.5in DP guns on 2×twin Mk IV twin turrets, 2×STAAG twin 40mm mountings, 2×twin 20mm, 10×21in torpedo tubes or two Squid AS mortars
Radars:	Types 293, 291, 275, 262
Machinery:	2×Foster Wheeler boilers (400lb/sq in/750°F), 2×shafts, Parsons geared turbines, 40,000shp
Speed/Range:	31kt/5,000nm @ 20kt
Oil Fuel (tons):	630
Complement:	280

5 The Modern Destroyer

At the end of the war in 1945 the Royal Navy possessed a destroyer fleet which was more than adequate for its peacetime tasks. In addition to ships already in service, most of which were fairly new, there were others at various stages of construction and development and these have been described in the preceding chapters. Despite the ready availability of ships such as the 'Battles', 'Weapons' and 'Darings' to meet the Navy's requirements, a number of other projects were considered in the decade following 1945.

The 'G' class has already been mentioned. The size and cost of the 'Daring' class was a constant source of worry and they were also considered too large for successful anti-submarine work. A proposal was therefore made for a new light destroyer, loosely based on the 'G' class, which would have a standard displacement of less than 2,000 tons, be armed with two twin 4.5in guns, six 40mm guns, one Pentad torpedo mounting and a Squid, and make 31kt on lightweight machinery with an output of 40,000shp. This would be achieved by reducing fuel bunkerage, ammunition supply and stores to save weight and reduce size although this would mean that the ships would be heavily dependent on depot ships like the prewar flotillas. Shades of this idea can be seen in the early proposals for the current Type 23 frigates which was originally conceived as a 'minimum frigate' dependent on accompanying ships for back-up facilities.

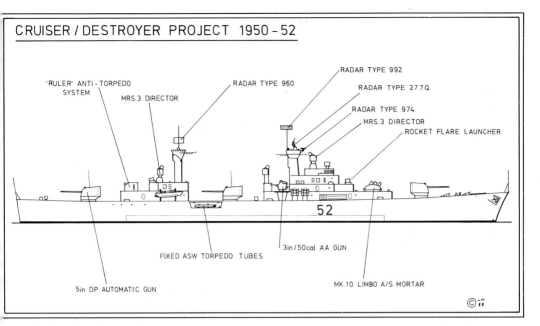

CRUISER / DESTROYER PROJECT 1950-52

'RULER' ANTI-TORPEDO SYSTEM
MRS.3 DIRECTOR
RADAR TYPE 960
RADAR TYPE 992
RADAR TYPE 277Q
RADAR TYPE 974
MRS.3 DIRECTOR
ROCKET FLARE LAUNCHER
52
FIXED ASW TORPEDO TUBES
3in/50cal AA GUN
5in DP AUTOMATIC GUN
MK.10 LIMBO A/S MORTAR

The light destroyer concept was updated in 1948 and was now armed with two single 5in guns, a new close range AA gun, eight torpedo tubes and a single Limbo. These changes increased standard displacement to around 2,500 tons — showing that a return to prewar dimensions was not a practical proposition for the modern destroyer.

The use of a 5in gun in this project was as a result of a 1948 decision to develop a new rapid fire, medium calibre gun to replace the 4.5in gun on new destroyer and cruiser projects. In order to achieve standardisation with the US Navy, the 5in calibre was selected and considerable work was carried out to perfect a suitable weapon. A 5in/62 calibre barrel was chosen and rate of fire was specified at 60 rounds per minute to be fired at a high muzzle velocity (3,200ft/sec or more). Any number of practical difficulties prevented this project from being completed, not least the question of overheating at such high rates of fire.

For close range AA work, the L70 version of the wartime 40mm/60 calibre Bofors was intended to form the basis of new single, twin and sextuple mountings. This gun was supposed to be effective out to 5,000yd but was never used by the Royal Navy, the close range defence requirement eventually being met by the Seacat missile. However, the L70 featured in a number of destroyer proposals until the late 1950s.

Apart from the light destroyer, other proposals were based on an updated and enlarged 'Daring' design to meet the requirement for a general purpose fleet destroyer. One example featured no less than four twin 4.5in guns and a Limbo AS mortar while still retaining two Pentad torpedo tubes and a good close range AA armament. Naturally this led to an increase in displacement which was estimated at between 3,500 and 4,000 tons. At the same time the Navy was examining various designs for new cruisers armed with the new fully automatic Mk 26 twin 6in turrets. Due to the weight of this installation, together with the need to incorporate adequate anti-aircraft defences, the size of these ships would be around 15,000 tons despite many attempts to produce the required attributes on a smaller hull. In 1949 the Assistant Chief of the Naval Staff proposed that a new type of ship, a cruiser/destroyer displacing around 5,000 tons and armed with the new automatic 5in gun, could replace both types. A considerable amount of work was done on this project which in its final form displaced 4,750 tons and was armed with two twin 5in and two twin 40mm/L70, each of the four gun mountings having its own MRS 3 fire control system. In a throwback to the early 'Battle' class, a single 4.5in gun was to be carried for target illumination. For ASW purposes two quadruple sets of AS torpedo tubes were supplemented by a single Limbo, and radar outfit included Type 960 long range, Types 277Q and 983 for aircraft direction and height finding, Type 992 target indicating and Type 974 navigation. Propulsion was by 60,000shp steam turbines giving a speed of 30kt at full load and a range of 3,000 miles at 20kt.

Work on the cruiser/destroyer continued until 1953 when further development was cancelled. However, the need for some new fleet escorts to replace the older wartime destroyers, which would begin to reach the end of their useful lives around

1958, was still apparent. One proposal was to build specialist ships for the anti-aircraft, anti-submarine and aircraft direction roles on a common hull, as had already been adopted in the 1951 frigate programme which was now under way and which produced the Type 12, 41 and 61 frigates. Although this project never came to fruition, partly because the Type 12 'Whitby' class (and the later 'Leanders') proved capable of carrying out the specialised ASW fleet escort role, work on the destroyer gave rise to the first work on combined steam and gas turbines (COSAG) machinery for modern warships.

In addition to the above, thoughts again turned to a general purpose fleet escort loosely based on an enlarged 'Daring' design. The first proposals were armed with three twin 4.5in, three twin 40mm/L70 supplemented by a number of single 40mm/60 Bofors, Limbo and 12 fixed torpedo tubes for anti-ship and anti-submarine use. A comprehensive radar outfit was also included. Propulsion machinery would be the new Y102 COSAG system giving a speed of just over 30kt on a displacement of 5,000 tons. Early in 1955 one twin 4.5in mounting and all the single Bofors guns were deleted in order to bring displacement down to 4,500 tons and the final crew complement would have been around 475 men. By mid-1955 work on the improved 'Daring' took a new direction following a decision to alter the design to incorporate the Seaslug long range surface-to-air guided missile system.

Seaslug, Britain's first naval guided missile, traced its development back as far as 1943 when it was realised that the new German stand-off weapons (eg FX1400 guided bomb), which sank and damaged many ships during the Salerno landings, posed an entirely new threat which could not be countered by contemporary gunnery systems. The requirement was to engage and destroy the carrying aircraft at long range before it could launch the missile. The only way to do this was by some form of guided missile, but the war ended before any workable system was produced and the project virtually died until revived in 1948. Prime contractor was the Armstrong Whitworth aircraft company which eventually ended up as part of the British Aerospace group while other companies involved were Sperry (guidance systems), GEC and Marconi (radars), and Vickers

Below:
The German FX 1400 guided bomb, which was first used with devastating effect in 1943, raised a requirement for a shipboard weapons system which could successfully engage the launching aircraft at long range. This led to the start of a development programme which eventually produced the Seaslug missile. *Author*

Right:
Sea trials for the Seaslug missile were carried out aboard HMS *Girdleness* in 1956-58. Converted from a Landing Craft Maintenance Ship, *Girdleness* was also intended to be the prototype of a convoy escort missile ship along the lines of the auxiliary AA cruisers used in World War 2. *Real Photos (S2589)*

Below right:
The Seaslug launcher eventually installed aboard the 'County' class destroyers was a heavy and complex affair, carrying two missiles instead of the triple arrangement in the trial installation aboard *Girdleness. C. & S. Taylor*

missile handling and launcher systems). As with most British missile systems in the postwar era, development was slow and the first test firing took place in Australia in 1954 followed by sea trials aboard the converted fleet auxiliary, *Girdleness*, between 1956 and 1958, by which time almost 100 Seaslugs had been fired. In its Mk 1 form the missile was 19ft 8in long and weighed approximately 4,000lb — almost 2 tons. The early prototypes had a liquid-fuelled sustainer rocket motor but this was replaced in production versions by a solid fuel motor. A notable feature of the missile was the use of four wrap-around solid fuel booster rockets positioned around the nose of the missile — an unusual arrangement intended to reduce stability and control problems during the launch phase.

The complete GWS 1 Seaslug missile system included a Type 901 target tracking and illuminating radar with a large distinctive 'searchlight' antenna. After launch the missile was gathered into the 901's beam and followed it all the way to

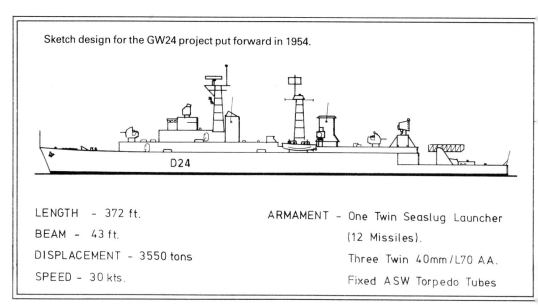

Sketch design for the GW24 project put forward in 1954.

D24

LENGTH - 372 ft.

BEAM - 43 ft.

DISPLACEMENT - 3550 tons

SPEED - 30 kts.

ARMAMENT - One Twin Seaslug Launcher

(12 Missiles).

Three Twin 40mm/L70 AA.

Fixed ASW Torpedo Tubes

the target. Maximum range of the Mk 1 was around 24 miles and this was increased to 36 miles in the later Mk 2 version.

Seaslug had a major impact on the development of RN cruiser and destroyer designs in the postwar era. In particular, the sheer size of the missile and its complicated handling arrangements made unprecedented space demands compared to traditional weapon systems. The complex and heavy tracking radars had to be located high up on the centreline, displacing other weapons and equipment. In order to stow a useful number of missiles, the carrying ship would need to be extremely large. One cruiser design in the 1950s, with a main armament of four 6in guns and carrying 48 Seaslug missiles, would have displaced 18,000 tons, while conversions of existing 'Colony' class ships would have been reduced to one 6in triple turret and stowage for only 24 missiles. At one stage, serious consideration was given to the conversion of the 'Majestic' class light carriers to missile ships carrying a total of 180 missiles serving two triple launchers.

At the other end of the scale, it appeared

initially that it would be impossible to install a worthwhile system in a destroyer-sized hull. One project put forward in 1954, designated GW24, was for a 3,550-ton ship armed with a Seaslug launcher (twin instead of triple) and magazine storage for only 12 missiles. Such was the impact of even this minimum system that the remaining armament consisted of only three twin 40mm/L70 mountings and two fixed torpedo tubes. Attempts to increase missile stowage resulted in a displacement of over 5,000 tons and a reduction in speed to 25-27kt which was not acceptable for fleet work.

In 1955 a proposal was made to take the design of the improved 'Daring' and modify it to take the lightweight Seaslug system devised for the GW24 design. The new project, initially known as GW54 with later variants designated GW55/56/57, was envisaged as a 4,550-ton ship carrying two Mk VI twin 4.5in mountings and 12 Seaslug missiles. Machinery would be the new Y102 COSAG arrangement. This design formed the basis of what was to become the 'County' class guided missile destroyer described below.

'County' Class Destroyers — *Antrim, Devonshire, Fife, Glamorgan, Hampshire, Kent, London, Norfolk*

Following on from the acceptance of the GW54 concept, orders for two fleet escorts were announced under the 1955-56 naval estimates but at this stage development of the basic design was still continuing. It was already apparent that the days of the large surface ship were numbered as far as the Royal Navy was concerned and it was

unlikely that any of the contemporary cruiser designs would ever be built. The Admiralty was therefore eager that the new ships should have the best all round capability possible. At one point consideration was given to carrying the new Type 984 long range '3D' radar (which was eventually fitted to the carriers *Eagle, Victorious* and *Hermes*)

Right:
HMS *London*, the last of the four Batch I ships, goes down the slipway at Swan Hunter's yard on the River Tyne on 7 December 1961. *Royal Navy*

Bottom:
The awkward arrangements for handling the Wessex helicopter can be seen in this view of the flightdeck of HMS *London*. With rotors and tailboom folded, the Wessex then had to be manhandled along the port side of the ship to the hangar which is just to the left of the Type 901 radar aerial. *Royal Navy*

so that the ships could act in the aircraft direction role although this would have necessitated the removal of the 4.5in guns.

By 1956 the design had grown to 5,980 tons (full load) and, apart from Seaslug, armament comprised two twin 4.5in, two twin 40mm/L70 with MRS 8 directors, eight DP fixed torpedo tubes and a Limbo AS mortar. A new Type 965 long range radar, together with a Type 277Q height finder, was enough for the aircraft direction role to be carried out. A Type 992 target indicating radar was to be carried while the 4.5in guns were controlled by an MRS3 director with Type 903 gunnery radar. Finally, of course, there was a single Type 901 associated with the GWS 1 Seaslug system. It would have been desirable to carry two Type 901s to give two separate control channels, but this was impossible without substantially increasing the size of the ship and, in addition, the slow rate of production of this equipment would have delayed completion of the ships.

This design was formally approved by the Admiralty Board in 1957 except for one major change involving the ship's ASW capability. Instead of the Limbo and fixed torpedo tubes, a Wessex helicopter was to be carried and this posed a difficult problem. The Wessex was one of the largest naval helicopters of its day but was equipped with its own radar and dipping sonar as

well as a range of ASW weapons including homing torpedoes. The removal of the Limbo, which was to have been mounted in a well just forward of the Seaslug launcher, left room for a minimum sized flight deck but provision of a hangar was more difficult as the 901 radar and its supporting structure occupied the most suitable position. The final arrangement was the insertion of a hangar between the 901 and the after funnel, which made the movement of the Wessex to and from the flight deck extremely awkward — particularly in rough weather.

The availability of the new Seacat close range surface-to-air missile led to another change while the ships were building and two quadruple launchers replaced the projected twin 40mm/L70 mountings. These were carried on the weather deck abreast the hangar and the associated GWS 21 directors positioned abaft the after funnel. This arrangement made the 'County' class the only British ships for many years to boast two separate guided missile systems.

The first two ships, *Devonshire* and *Hampshire*, were laid down in 1959 and completed in 1962 and 1963 respectively. There is no doubt that the 'County' class were among the most handsome ships ever produced for the Royal Navy, but they were certainly different from anything which had gone before. The two most obvious features were the full lines of the hull with its very high freeboard and the two squat, rounded funnels. The shape of the hull was dictated to a large extent by the horizontal stowage of the 30 Seaslug missiles in a hangar-like magazine running most of the length of the ship. This layout required new arrangements for magazine safety as it represented a considerable departure from previous practice.

The two funnels were an external indication of the machinery layout which featured two Y102 steam plants forward, each incorporating two G6 gas turbines aft. Apart from the contemporary Type 81 'Tribal' class frigates, this represented the first use of gas turbines in the propulsion of a major warship. Each of the two shafts was driven by a 15,000shp steam turbine and two 7,500shp gas turbines, giving a total output of 60,000shp for a speed of 30kt at full load. The gas turbines were intended to act as boosters to the main steam plant when high speeds were required with the steam turbines being used for normal cruising. In addition the G6s allowed the ship to be got underway at short notice without the previous long wait while adequate steam pressure was raised, and also provided a degree of redundancy in the event of action damage.

Following orders for the first pair of 'County' class destroyers, a further pair (*London* and *Kent*) were ordered under the 1956-57 Estimates and were laid down in 1960, being completed in 1963.

The building time of just over three years was very creditable bearing in mind the size and complexity of these ships, particularly when compared with the building times of the later Type 42 destroyers which were smaller and benefited from developments in shipbuilding technology. With an overall length of 520ft, a standard displacement of over 5,000 tons and a complement of nearly 500 men, these ships were generally regarded as being closer to a light cruiser than a destroyer. There was some truth in this point of view and in fact the 'Counties' were perhaps the natural outcome of the cruiser/destroyer concept. Originally they were designated guided missile armed destroyers (abbreviated to GMD) and were later referred to as DLGs (Destroyer Leader, Guided Missile) to conform with American practice. In later life they were often classified as light cruisers and because of their size were often used as task force flagships after the demise of the Royal Navy's conventional cruisers. This was facilitated by the layout of the bridge area which featured a small enclosed pilot bridge with good all-round vision above the main bridge which spanned the full width of the forward superstructure. The latter was often used as a flag bridge by any Admiral who was embarked as task force commander.

Deep in the bowels of the ship was the Action Information Centre with its rows of radar consoles and an adjoining sonar room just forward of it. This operations room could be reached directly from the bridge by a lift. Accommodation standards were much improved with full air conditioning and bunk beds for most of the crew. Nevertheless the lower messdecks were still extremely cramped due to the enormous space demands of the various weapon systems.

After the first four ships had been ordered, there was a delay in the programme as the design was further modified to take advantage of improvements offered by the Mk 2 version of the Seaslug.

Top right:
Apart from Seaslug, the 'County' class also carried two GWS 21 Seacat missile systems for close range defence — thus making them the first British ships to be armed with two separate missile systems.
Short Bros

Above right:
HMS *Devonshire* was the first of the 'County' class to enter service, in 1962. The first four ships carried a Type 992 target indicator radar on the foremast and an AKE-1 aerial for the Type 965 on the mainmast.
Royal Navy

Right:
HMS *Hampshire*, photographed at Malta in 1976, was the second ship to commission. She was the first of the class to be scrapped, in 1976, after only 13 years service. *Royal Navy*

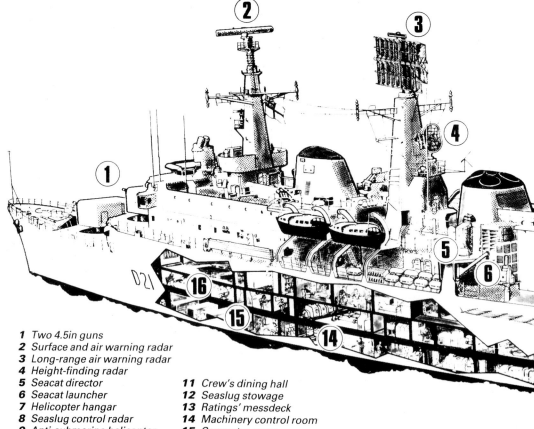

1 Two 4.5in guns
2 Surface and air warning radar
3 Long-range air warning radar
4 Height-finding radar
5 Seacat director
6 Seacat launcher
7 Helicopter hangar
8 Seaslug control radar
9 Anti-submarine helicopter
10 Seaslug launcher

11 Crew's dining hall
12 Seaslug stowage
13 Ratings' messdeck
14 Machinery control room
15 Computer room
16 Operations room

Far left:
Despite the adoption of the guided missile, the two Mk VI twin 4.5in gun turrets were still an important part of the ship's armament. Note the MRS 3 Director above the bridge, also trained to starboard with the guns. *Royal Navy*

Left:
A dramatic shot showing a Seaslug being fired from HMS *Glamorgan*. At this stage the missile is still being accelerated under the thrust of the four booster motors wrapped around the nose.
Royal Navy

nd new developments in electronic warfare. Consequently the next two ships (*Glamorgan* and *ife*) were not laid down until 1962 for eventual completion in 1966. By this time there were onsiderable financial constraints on the construction of new ships with the 'Leander' frigate programme underway and expensive modernisation programmes for the fleet carriers *Ark Royal* nd *Eagle* to be completed. Consequently the last wo ships of the class, *Antrim* and *Norfolk* were ot approved until 1964 and were only laid down in 966 for eventual completion in 1970.

Apart from carrying the Seaslug Mk 2, the last four ships featured a number of external differences — the most obvious of which were the revisions to the radar outfit. The original layout consisted of a mainmast amidships carrying an AKE-1 aerial for the Type 965 aerial and a Type 277Q heightfinding radar. The foremast carried a streamlined 'cheese' aerial for the original Type 992, a navigation radar and a polemast with communications, ESM and UHF/DF equipment. For weapons control there was a Type 903 on the MRS 3 director above the bridge, Type 262 on the Seacat directors and Type 901 for target and missile tracking right aft. On the last four ships these arrangements were modified, mainly by the use of the larger AKE-2 'double bedstead' aerial for the Type 965. This in turn necessitated the use of a wider and stronger mainmast and the Type 277Q mounted on the after side was replaced by an improved version, the Type 278. A new, taller foremast carried a Type 992Q, which was an updated version of the earlier 992, featuring a new slim, cylindrical aerial. This was mounted right at the top of the mast and ESM equipment was located below. The Seacat GWS 22 replaced earlier GWS 21, the main difference being the use of a Type 903 tracking radar instead of the Type 262.

Like most warships, the 'Counties' were modified during their service lives. In the

system installed. However, they did not match up to the Exocet-equipped ships, particularly as the Mk 1 Seaslug's performance was inadequate by the standards of the day. In addition, each of the 'Counties' made a heavy demand on manpower — a commodity under increasing pressure as successive major defence cuts reduced the overall size of the Navy. Consequently, most of the four Batch I ships, to use the term which came into vogue during the 1970s, were paid off well before the end of their normally accepted operational lifespan. *Hampshire* was the first to go in 1976 after only 13 years in service. *Devonshire* paid off in 1978 and was listed for disposal and *London* decommissioned in 1980 before being sold to Pakistan and renamed *Babur* in 1982. Due to lack of spares the Seaslug Mk 1 system was deactivated and an Alouette III helicopter was employed instead of the Wessex. The ship is now used as a training vessel with the Seaslug magazine converted to accommodation for cadets. *Devonshire* was also the subject of sale negotiations with Egypt which intended to convert her to carry up to six Lynx helicopters by removing the Seaslug launcher and using the magazine as a hangar. However, this deal fell through and the ship was eventually sunk in 1985 while being used as a target for the Sea Eagle air-to-surface missile and a Tigerfish torpedo fired from the submarine *Splendid*.

The remaining Batch I ship, *Kent*, was seriously damaged by a fire while undergoing refit at Portsmouth in 1976. She was subsequently repaired at Wallsend but then became a harbour training ship in 1980. Later deactivated, she was used as an accommodation ship at Portsmouth for many years and is now used as a static accommodation and training ship by the Sea Cadet Corps.

Of the Batch II ships, *Antrim* and *Glamorgan* were in action during the Falklands War; *Norfolk* had been sold to Chile only a few months before and *Fife* was undergoing a refit at the time. *Antrim* was flagship for Operation 'Paraquat', the recovery of South Georgia, and was later present during the San Carlos landings when she was hit by a 1,000lb bomb which, fortunately, did not explode. However, there was considerable damage which kept the ship out of front line duties for most of the remainder of the fighting. *Glamorgan* entered the fray on 1 May 1982, when she took part in a bombardment on the Port Stanley area and was damaged by some near misses. However, she remained in action almost to the end of the war, carrying out many bombardments and supporting the Pebble Island raid. However, on 12 June she

mid-1960s they were all fitted with two single 20mm guns high up abaft the bridge in order to provide a suitable weapon for peacetime patrol duties. This was a result of experience gained in the Far East where the 'County' class were often deployed. Following the sinking of the Israeli destroyer *Eilat* in 1967, all Royal Navy warships were gradually fitted with the Corvus multi-barrelled chaff launcher system as a passive defence against anti-ship missiles. In the 'Counties' these were mounted on platforms abreast the fore funnel.

In 1970, the new Conservative Government, concerned about the fleet's lack of striking power against surface ships due to the run down of the carrier fleet, opened negotiations for the purchase of the French Exocet surface-to-surface missile. Subsequently a substantial number were ordered and HMS *Norfolk* was selected for the first installation. In 1972-73 she underwent a refit which included the removal of B turret so that four Exocet container launchers could be mounted immediately before the bridge. First test firings were made off Toulon in 1974 and eventually *Antrim, Fife* and *Glamorgan* were also rearmed with Exocets, giving these ships no less than three separate missile systems.

The older ships were not converted to carry Exocets although they did receive some updating of their radar equipment with Type 992Q replacing the older 992 and the updated GWS 22 Seacat

Above:
The ship's Wessex helicopter was an effective anti-submarine system in its own right. Although the ship carried a comprehensive range of sonars, the helicopter would localise the contact and carry out an attack with depth charges or homing torpedoes. *Royal Navy*

Below:
HMS *Norfolk* was the first of the class to be fitted with the French Exocet missile. This installation necessitated the removal of B turret. This photo was taken in 1978, by which time the ship has also been equipped with the SCOT communications system; the aerials can be seen abreast the mainmast. *Royal Navy*

was hit by an Exocet missile fired from a land based launcher as she withdrew from a NGS mission. The quick action of the officer of the watch in turning the ship stern-on to the approaching missile undoubtedly saved the ship although there were many casualties as the missile exploded in the hangar area. During her many actions she fired no less than 1,450 4.5in rounds and seven Seaslugs, although no enemy aircraft were destroyed by the latter. In fact, the Seaslug was in effect used as a barrage defence weapon with the missiles' boosters scattering over the sky in the path of approaching aircraft, putting them off their aim even if they were not hit.

After the Falklands War, both ships underwent a refit and, together with *Fife*, incorporated some of the lessons learnt in that conflict. New Super RBOC chaff launchers were fitted on a platform built on the side of the superstructure abreast the foremast. The ship's ASW capability was transformed by the addition of the STWS-1 AS torpedo system, with triple 12.75in tubes amidships on either beam, and the aged Wessex helicopters were replaced by the more modern Lynx (which was not sonar equipped). However, the declining status of these ships was illustrated by the fact that *Glamorgan* lost her Seacat missiles and these were replaced by two single 40mm guns mounted on the platforms formerly occupied by the missile directors.

Despite the Falklands experience, the number of destroyers and frigates continued to fall and the 'Counties' still made heavy demands on manpower, having almost twice the complement of a Type 42. Also, of course, the Seaslug was now completely obsolete and so it was no surprise when *Antrim* paid off in 1984 and was sold to Chile in September of that year for £5 million. *Glamorgan* continued for a little longer, seeing some action as she supported British peacekeeping forces in the Lebanon during 1984. She finally paid off in September 1986 and was also sold to Chile, being renamed *Admirante Latorre*. In the meantime *Norfolk* (renamed *Prat* when sold to Chile in 1982) had run aground and was badly damaged so the Chilean Navy expressed an interest in obtaining the remaining Royal Navy 'County' class ship, *Fife*. In June 1986, *Fife* had completed a refit at Portsmouth and had been converted to a cadet training ship. The Seaslug system had been removed and extra accommodation provided in the former magazine and in a deckhouse built on the quarterdeck to replace the missile launcher. In this form the ship carried out a series of training cruises, culminating in a visit to North America and the Great Lakes in 1987 before returning to

the UK and paying off at Portsmouth in June 1987. She was then sold to the Chilean Navy and renamed *Blanco Encalada*.

The 'County' class destroyers were fine ships but suffered from the progressive obsolescence of the Seaslug missile system and the cost of maintaining large crews at a time of financial stringency. In addition, the propulsion machinery was temperamental and caused many problems. Nevertheless, they were almost all sold off before reaching the end of their useful lives and without any consideration being given to their modernisation or conversion to other roles — a sad end to ships which brought the Royal Navy into the missile age.

Name	No	Laid Down	Launched	Completed	Builder	Yard	Remarks	
Antrim	D18	20/01/66	19/10/67	14/07/70	Fairfield	Govan, Clyde	Sold to Chile 1984	
Devonshire	D02	09/03/59	10/06/60	15/11/62	Cammell Laird	Birkenhead	Expended as target ship	1985
Fife	D20	31/05/62	09/07/64	21/06/66	Fairfield	Govan, Clyde	Sold to Chile 1987	
Glamorgan	D19	13/09/62	09/07/64	13/10/66	Vickers Armstrong	Tyne	Sold to Chile 1986	
Hampshire	D06	26/03/59	16/03/61	15/03/63	J. Brown	Clydebank	Scrapped Briton Ferry	1976
Kent	D12	01/03/60	27/09/61	15/08/63	Harland & Wolf	Belfast	Static training hulk	
London	D16	26/02/60	07/12/61	14/11/63	Swan Hunter	Tyne	PN 1982. Cadet Training Ship	
Norfolk	D21	15/03/66	16/11/67	07/03/70	Swan Hunter	Tyne	To Chile 1982. Laid up.	

Data: 'County' class, HMS *Norfolk* (1974)

Displacement (tons): 5,440 standard, 6,200 full load

Length/Beam (ft): 520.5 (oa)/54

Draught (ft): 20 (full load)

Armament: 4×4.5in guns (2×2), 2×20mm guns, 4×Exocet SSM, Seaslug Mk 2 SAM system, twin launcher, 2×GWS24 Seacat SAM systems, 2×quad launchers

Aircraft: 1×Wessex HAS 3 helicopter

Radars: Types 965 (AKE-2), 278, 992Q, 903, 901

Machinery: COSAG, 2×Babcock & Wilcox boilers, 2×steam turbines (30,000shp), 4×G6 gas turbines (30,000shp). Total 60,000shp

Speed/Range: 30kt/3,500nm @ 28kt

Oil Fuel (tons): 600

Complement: 470

Below:
In 1983 HMS *Fife* completed a refit in which provision was made for the operation of a Lynx helicopter instead of the Wessex and triple ASW torpedo launchers were installed on either beam. In 1986 her Seaslug launcher was removed and the missile magazine was converted to messdecks so that she could be used as a Cadet Training Ship. *M. Lennon*

Type 82 Destroyer — *Bristol*

At the time the 'County' class destroyer design was finalised and the first two ships ordered, it was envisaged that a total of 12 missile-armed fleet escorts would be required by the mid-1960s to supplement the eight 'Daring' class ships as it was assumed that all the older destroyers would, by then, have been scrapped or converted to frigates. In fact, as has been recounted, the need for destroyers and fleet aircraft direction escorts had been partly met by the conversion of the four 'Battle' class ships and the modernisation of the 'Ca' class destroyers. Nevertheless, new ships would be needed as the older ships only had limited lives and so design work commenced in

1961 on a new missile-armed destroyer which would eventually follow the 'Counties' into service. The new design was loosely based on the layout of the earlier ships and was particularly intended as an escort to the new class of aircraft carrier then under development (CVA-01).

The new Type 82 — this was the first time that a destroyer had been given a frigate-type designation — was of similar size to the 'County' class and had a COSAG propulsion system although the gas turbine element was provided by two 22,000shp TM1A Olympus units. The boiler uptakes passed up through the large fore funnel while the Olympus exhaust was fed to two after funnels situated side by side. This gave rise to the unique three-funnel arrangement which characterised the ship, although a similar layout had been considered and rejected for the 'County' class.

The major improvements in the Type 82 related to the armament which featured three completely new weapon systems — the Sea Dart surface-to-air missile, the Ikara anti-submarine missile and a new automatic 4.5in gun. No provision was made for a

Below:
A 1966 artist's impression of the Type 82 destroyer. The most prominent feature is the huge dome covering the Anglo-Dutch 3D long range radar which was intended to equip this ship but which was subsequently cancelled. *Real Photos (N4010)*

Bottom:
HMS *Bristol* was the sole Type 82 to be built and initially acted as a trials ship for the new weapon systems including the Ikara and Sea Dart missile systems. Note the Type 965 radar atop the bridge which was fitted in lieu of the original Anglo-Dutch radar. *C. & S. Taylor*

helicopter but a Limbo mortar was carried in a well on the quarterdeck. This was the last major British warship to be built which was not capable of operating a helicopter — a strange omission in retrospect, but presumably it was thought that the long range Ikara system would fill the gap at considerably less cost. This was probably true at the time but today's improved sonars require engagement far beyond Ikara's 10-mile range.

Ikara basically consists of a small delta-winged, rocket-propelled launch vehicle which carries a Mk 44 or Mk 46 homing torpedo. Following detection and localisation of a submarine target, the missile is launched towards the target position which is continually updated during the flight time. When in the target vicinity the torpedo is released and then homes in on it in the normal manner.

The Sea Dart missile, originally designated CF299, is a vast improvement over the earlier Seaslug, being lighter, smaller, longer-ranged and more accurate. Boosted off its twin launcher by a 35,000lb thrust rocket motor, the missile, powered by a Rolls-Royce Odin ramjet, flies towards the target at a speed of Mach 3.5. Maximum range is in

the region of 50 miles. Sea Dart uses a semi-active guidance system whereby the missile homes on to signals reflected from the target by the ship's Type 909 target illuminating radar. Using this method, accuracy improves as the missile gets closer to the target, unlike the beam-riding Seaslug which loses accuracy as the radar beam widens out in proportion to its distance from the ship. The smaller size of the Sea Dart means that more rounds can be stowed in less space and handling procedures are simpler.

The Mk 8 automatic 4.5in gun had been under development for some time but was not intended as an AA weapon, having only 55° elevation. It was primarily meant for anti-ship and shore bombardment purposes. Bearing in mind the struggle during the 1940s to perfect a working high-angle mounting, this may appear to have been a retrograde step. However, the theory was that the guided missile had taken over the air defence role. Although the Falklands experience showed that this was not completely true, it did make any form of dive-bombing suicidal and therefore the gun was only called upon to engage low-level targets which did not require high angles of elevation. The Mk 8 was designed to be a very reliable system as most ships would only carry a single mounting and therefore its rate of fire was kept down to 25 rounds per minute — a low figure compared with some contemporary weapons, but quite sufficient for the NGS and anti-ship role.

Another feature which the Type 82 introduced was not externally apparent. This was an Action Data Automated Weapons System (ADAWS2 in this case) which integrated the tracking and engagement of targets under one computer-controlled system. The 'County' class had been equipped with a rudimentary action data system but it relied heavily on the manual insertion and update of data. ADAWS2 could accept data from the ship's radars (Types 965, 992 and 909) and sonars (Types 170, 184), and produce a continuous track history for each target. Using this information, it could carry out an evaluation of the relative threat of each contact and control the engagement using the relevant weapon system. ADAWS2 was based on two Ferranti FM1600 computers.

Initial plans called for four new Type 82s with the possibility of a further four which would supplement and eventually replace the first four 'County' class ships. However, the Labour Government's decision, in 1966, to cancel CVA-01 and to run down the carrier force over the next few years effectively removed the requirement for

Above:
Another aerial view showing the layout of the forecastle with the Mk 8 automatic 4.5in gun and circular zareba for the Ikara launcher. *Royal Navy*

Left:
The machinery control room (MCR) enables the Olympus gas turbines and the steam plant to be operated by remote control. *Royal Navy*

class destroyers and later 'Kortenaer' class frigates with the Olympus, the radar project died for a combination of technical and financial reasons. Consequently, HMS *Bristol* eventually received the standard Type 965 with the AKE-2 aerial.

Bristol was launched in 1969 and commissioned in 1973, although her trials status was emphasised by the lack of much of the ECM and ESM equipment which was standard in operational ships of the time. Her early career was dogged by ill fortune and in November 1974 her steam plant was destroyed in a serious fire. In a graphic demonstration of the flexibility of the gas turbine as a ship's prime mover, *Bristol* was able to continue with her trials programme using only the Olympus engines until a major refit in 1976-77 when the steam plant was repaired. Two years later she was at last upgraded to fully operational status with the addition of Corvus chaff launchers, UAA-1 ESM equipment on the mainmast and two single 20mm guns on new platforms below the bridge. At the same time the Limbo mortar was removed and the deck was plated over to form a

these ships. Despite this, one ship, HMS *Bristol*, was ordered on 4 October 1966 and laid down the following year. The main reason for this was to allow the ship to act as a trials platform for the various new weapons systems and electronics. Originally it had been intended that the Type 82 would carry a new 3D long range radar, then the subject of a joint Anglo-Dutch development programme. In return for buying this radar, it was hoped that the Dutch Navy could be persuaded to buy the Olympus gas turbine and Sea Dart missile system for the new destroyers which they were also building. In the end, the Dutch decided that the Sea Dart was not suitable for their purposes and, although they subsequently equipped the 'Tromp'

helicopter landing deck. There were still no hangarage facilities so there was no question of the ship operating its own helicopter, but at least helicopters could land for the purposes of transferring stores and personnel.

In this form *Bristol* recommissioned at the end of 1980 and was subsequently often used as a task force flagship as her size made it easy to absorb the extra staff members embarked for this role. Thus, in 1981, she was the flagship of Vice Admiral J. Cox (Flag Officer 3rd Flotilla) during Exercise 'Ocean Safari 81'. After a short refit early in 1982, she joined the Falklands Task Force on 25 May, operating with the Carrier Battle Group until the end of the war when she again became a flagship, this time flying the flag of Rear-Adm D. Refell who commanded the remaining naval force. Later that year the ship returned to the UK and during a short refit her light AA armament was increased by the addition of two twin BMARC/Oerlikon 30mm mountings and two single GAM-B01 20mm guns.

Returning to service early in 1983, she made several overseas deployments before paying off in July 1984 for a major two-year refit. Immediately prior to this she suffered a major explosion in her boiler room which seriously injured three seamen

and caused extensive damage. This was repaired during the refit and other work included the installation of a new Type 1022 radar, to replace the original Type 965, and the removal of the Ikara ASW missile system. More significant was the work which was not done. It had been expected that the close range armament would have been boosted by the first RN installation of the Vulcan Phalanx CIWS, and the ASW capability partly restored by the addition of the STWS-1 system with two sets of triple AS torpedo tubes. However, these modifications were not incorporated and the ship recommissioned in early 1986 with no ASW capability at all. The following year *Bristol* was further modified to replace the 'County' class destroyer *Fife* as Dartmouth training ship, a role she took up in September 1987 and continues to carry out at the time of writing.

HMS *Bristol* has always been something of a white elephant in the fleet — inevitable as the only ship of her class — and her present role as a training ship probably marks the twilight of her career. Nevertheless, she performed a useful role in her early days as a trials ship for the new weapon systems. It is unfortunate that her weapon outfit was not kept fully up to date as she is one of the few ships in the fleet large enough to accept modifications and extra fittings without serious repercussions on stability and internal space.

Above left:
Over the years, HMS *Bristol* was extensively modified. This 1986 picture shows the Limbo removed, a new Type 1022 radar above the bridge and new close range AA weapons on a platform abreast the funnels. *Royal Navy*

Left:
HMS *Bristol* is currently employed as a Cadet Training Ship, having taken over the role from the 'County' class destroyer *Fife*. An extra messdeck has been added between the forward Type 909 dome and the bridge, and the Ikara missile system has been removed. *HMS* Bristol

Below:
HMS *Bristol* runs alongside the RFA *Gold Rover* during a RAS exercise for the benefit of the embarked cadets. *HMS* Bristol

Data:	Type 82, HMS *Bristol* (1973)
Displacement (tons):	6,100 standard, 7,100 full load
Length/Beam (ft):	507 (oa)/55
Draught (ft):	22.5 (full load)
Armament:	1×Mk 8 automatic 4.5in gun, Sea Dart GWS 30 SAM system, 1×twin launcher, Ikara AS missile system, Mk 10 Limbo AS mortar
Radars:	Types 965 (AKE-2), 992Q, 909(2), 978
Machinery:	COSAG. 2×Babcock & Wilcox boilers, geared steam turbines (30,000shp), 2×Olympus gas turbines (44,000shp)
Speed/Range:	30kt/5,000nm @ 18kt
Oil Fuel (tons):	900
Complement:	433

Type 42 Destroyers (Batch I) — *Sheffield, Birmingham, Cardiff, Coventry, Glasgow, Newcastle.* (Batch II) — *Exeter, Southampton, Nottingham, Liverpool.* (Batch III) — *Manchester, Gloucester, York, Edinburgh*

The demise of the CVA-01 carrier programme and the cancellation of all but one Type 82 destroyer — both politically motivated decisions — left the Royal Navy with a potential situation where it would be seriously lacking in any effective form of defence against air attack. The fleet air defence provided by the carrier's fighters and airborne early warning aircraft would soon disappear and the limitations of the Seaslug surface-to-air missile aboard the 'County' class ships were already recognised. In these circumstances it was vital to get the new Sea Dart missile into service as soon as possible so that it would be available in the mid-1970s when it was expected that the last of the carriers would have paid off.

Sea Dart was an effective weapon system and had originally been intended for installation in frigate-sized ships such as those of the 'Leander' class where it would replace the helicopter hangar and Limbo mortar. However, the GWS30 (the designation given to the complete missile system including launchers, magazines, radars and fire control) outgrew this proposal and it was obvious that a destroyer-sized ship would be required. The government accepted the requirement for deployment of the Sea Dart but imposed a cost limit of £11 million (1967 prices) on each ship. The resulting Type 42 destroyer reflected this artificial restriction in many ways, being extremely cramped from the accommodation point of view and having no margin for future modifications and modernisation.

The final design was a compromise in many ways, representing the minimum ship which would get the GWS30 system to sea, and was similar in outline to a private venture design proposed by Vickers in 1966 — the Type 3009. Apart from the Sea Dart missile, the Type 42 was also armed with the Mk 8 automatic 4.5in gun and had a hangar and flightdeck intended for the operation of a Lynx helicopter. The only other armament consisted of two single 20mm guns in the bridge wings. Even at the time of their inception, these ships were criticised as being under-armed for their size and role and, although provision was made for AS torpedo tubes, these were not fitted initially in the early ships. The Lynx helicopter was also not available until 1978 and the less capable Wasp was carried when the early ships commissioned. Finally, Corvus chaff launchers were disposed on either beam abreast the hangar.

To support the weapon systems, a comprehensive radar outfit was provided. The main search radar was the evergreen Type 965 — verging on the obsolete even at this time — and a Type 992Q target indicating radar on the mainmast. For target tracking and engagement by missile or gun, two Type 909 radars were mounted fore and aft enclosed in weatherproof domes. This was actually a substantial improvement on the arrangements in both *Bristol* and the 'County' class which each only carried one radar for the control of a missile engagement. In the Type 42 it was possible to simultaneously engage two separate targets with the Sea Dart missiles — these and other actions being controlled by an ADAWS-4 automatic system. This was similar to the ADAWS-2 installed aboard HMS *Bristol* except that there was no provision for the control of an Ikara missile.

Sonars included a Type 184M medium frequency set with a 360° scanning capability and a Type 162 bottomed-target classification set. These were used to direct torpedo attacks by the ship's helicopter and, later, in conjunction with the STWS-1 ASW torpedo system.

The armament and electronic outfit described above illustrate the change in the nature of naval warfare brought about by missiles, electronics and computers. Although not as large as the preceding missile-armed destroyers, the Type 42 offered a more effective missile system and an equivalent gunnery capability. However, it lacked the close range defences of the 'Counties' (Seacat missiles) and the Ikara missile system of the Type 82 although this was compensated for by the addition of the helicopter. On balance they were better value for money than HMS *Bristol* although lacking that ship's potential for updating and modernisation.

Top right:
HMS *Sheffield* was the first of the Type 42 destroyers and was launched in 1971. The shortness of the forecastle and the relatively light armament are apparent in this aerial view. *Royal Navy*

Above right:
With the weatherproof domes removed, HMS *Cardiff's* Type 909 tracking radars are clearly visible fore and aft. In addition the ship carries a Type 965 radar forward and a Type 992Q on the mainmast. *Royal Navy*

Right:
The Type 42's Lynx helicopter was originally intended for anti-submarine purposes, although it was not sonar equipped. More recently, it has been adapted to fire the air-to-surface Sea Skua missile which scored several successes in the Falklands. *Author*

One factor which reduced the size of the hull and also had the effect of reducing manning requirements was the decision to adopt an all-gas turbine propulsion system. The Royal Navy had amassed a considerable amount of experience with gas turbines aboard the 'Counties' and the Type 81 frigates and further data was obtained from the frigate HMS *Exmouth* which was converted in 1967 as the Navy's first all-gas turbine warship (apart from various experimental coastal craft) with a Rolls-Royce Marine Olympus and two Proteus engines. The Type 42 was equipped with a two-shaft arrangement, each driven by an Olympus TM3B and Tyne RM1A in a COGAG arrangement giving a total output of almost 60,000shp. Speed at full load was 30kt.

The use of gas turbines had a major impact on the layout of the ship due to the large ducts required for intakes and exhausts. A forward turbine room housed the two Olympus engines facing forward with the exhausts trunked to the single broad funnel. The two Tyne engines were in the after turbine room with their intakes aft and the exhausts leading forward into the funnel. This space also contained the enormous gearboxes, which took the drive from either the Olympus or the Tyne and transferred power to the shaft. Auxiliary machinery spaces, fore and aft of the turbine rooms, housed four Paxman/GEC diesel generators and the air conditioning and water distillation plants. Above decks, the gas turbine inlet trunkings incorporated bulky filter installations fore and aft of the funnel. Thus the whole of the midships section above and below decks was taken up by the ship's machinery, restricting the space available for weapon platforms. Taken with the need to position a flightdeck and hangar right aft, the layout of the ship was firmly fixed in the early stages.

The building programme proceeded with painful slowness — a feature of many postwar programmes. Although the first ship, *Sheffield*, was ordered in 1968, she was not laid down until 1970 and construction took over five years. Orders for a further five were placed during the course of 1971 but the last of these was not completed until 1979. Part of the reason for the early delay in the programme was the diversion of resources to the construction of two Type 42s for the Argentinian Navy. These were ordered in 1970 with the intention of the first ship being built by Vickers at Barrow-in-Furness and the other at Rio Santiago in Argentina with British technical assistance. At the time this order was greeted with great enthusiasm as it represented the first overseas sale of a British destroyer design for over a decade. History was to show that it was not quite the success that it appeared at the time, although nobody could have foreseen that these ships would be ranged against the Royal Navy during the Falklands War in 1982.

No further orders were forthcoming until 1976 when two ships were ordered, followed by contracts for a further two the following year. These four comprised the Batch II Type 42s and differed from the earlier ships mainly in respect of having an improved electronics fit. The Type 965 was replaced by the new Type 1022 which had a much improved performance, particularly in picking out targets against a background of clutter and interference produced by unwanted returns or enemy jamming. An important, but less obvious, change was the updated ADAWS-7 system which featured improved software and enhanced the effectiveness of the various weapon systems. All the Batch II ships were completed with the

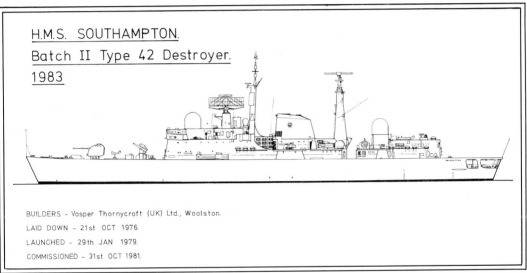

H.M.S. SOUTHAMPTON.

Batch II Type 42 Destroyer.

1983

BUILDERS - Vosper Thornycroft (UK) Ltd., Woolston.

LAID DOWN - 21st OCT 1976.

LAUNCHED - 29th JAN 1979.

COMMISSIONED - 31st OCT 1981.

STWS-1 ASW torpedo system and shipped a Lynx helicopter on commissioning. Only two ships, *Exeter* and *Southampton*, had been completed by the outbreak of the Falklands War and only *Exeter* was fully operational although completion of the remaining pair was brought forward as a result of the fighting. Indeed, *Liverpool* was handed over almost a year ahead of schedule.

The last four Type 42s (Batch III) were ordered between 1978 and 1980 and were instantly recognisable by their lengthened hulls, which were 41ft longer than those of the standard ships. In fact this was not so much a modification as a reversion to the design as originally envisaged. At an early stage in the design phase of the Type 42, a decision had been made, under pressure to cut costs, to shorten the hull by reducing the size and capacity of the Sea Dart magazine. In fact the cost savings this afforded were minimal and the result was that the early Type 42s were uncomfortable and wet in a seaway due to a lack of hydrodynamic lift at the bow. Experience showed that the extra volume of a longer bow would restore buoyancy and allow

additional Sea Darts to be stowed. As it was shown that the extra cost could be kept within reasonable limits, development of the Batch III design was allowed. The opportunity was taken to incorporate a few other changes, notably the replacement of the Type 184 sonar with the newer Type 2016 and the adoption of a square-transom stern which allowed an increase in flightdeck area. In other respects these ships were similar to the previous Batch II version.

Prior to the Falklands War the ships in service were little changed from their original configuration, but experience in the South Atlantic brought about significant alterations. No less than five Type 42s took part in the war (*Sheffield, Coventry, Exeter, Glasgow, Cardiff*) where they were employed as fleet escorts, radar pickets and gunfire support ships and also undertook the protection of the amphibious forces as they established a beachhead at San Carlos during May 1982. *Sheffield* was tragically sunk during the early stages of the operation. Hit on 4 May by an air-launched Exocet, she later foundered while under tow to

South Georgia. On 25 May *Coventry* was sunk during a concentrated air attack while acting as a forward missile trap against enemy aircraft attempting to reach the San Carlos area. This latter sinking highlighted the Type 42's lack of a suitable point defence weapon system (such as the Seawolf missile). To rectify this, *Coventry* was operating in company with the Type 22 frigate *Broadsword* whose Seawolfs were intended to provide close range protection for the destroyer. As the ships manoeuvred to avoid incoming aircraft, *Coventry* crossed ahead of the frigate causing the Seawolf radars to lose their lock on the aircraft. This allowed an Argentinian Skyhawk to run in and place three bombs straight into the port side of the *Coventry* which immediately settled in the water, sinking within 15min. Fortunately most of her crew were saved, although 19 men were killed.

Of the other ships, *Glasgow* was hit on 12 May by a 1,000lb bomb which fortunately passed right through the after machinery room without exploding — the ship would almost certainly have been lost if it had. As it was, hasty repairs were carried out and the ship remained in action for a few more days until relieved by *Exeter*. The latter ship was involved in the fighting up to the end of the war and had some notable successes with her Sea Darts, illustrating the superior performance of the Type 1022 radar and the ADAWS-7 action information system. *Cardiff* was employed mostly as an escort for the carrier force, but also carried out a number of NGS missions and at the end of hostilities she was the first British ship to enter Port Stanley, escorting the liner *Canberra*.

As a result of the Falklands War, all Type 42s were modified to increase their close range AA armament. All the ships' boats were landed to make room for new weapon platforms abreast the funnel where a BMARC GCM-A03 twin 30mm mounting was installed on either beam. In addition a single BMARC GAM-B01 20mm gun was mounted on either side of the after superstructure, adjacent to the Corvus chaff launchers which were also supplemented by the addition of Tracor Super RBOC chaff launchers abaft the bridge. In the longer term, all the surviving Batch I ships, starting with *Cardiff*, were fitted with the Type 1022 radar and ADAWS-7 to replace the earlier installations.

The armament changes outlined above were also incorporated in the Batch II ships as they were due for refitting. Of the Batch III ships, *Manchester* was completed with the original armament layout but was almost immediately modified by the addition of the 20mm and 30mm guns, although in this case the new GAM-B01 20mm guns were mounted in the bridge wings, displacing the original World War 2 pattern 20mm guns to new

platforms on either side of the after end of the hangar. The remaining three ships were completed to this altered configuration and, in addition, carried the new Sea Gnat decoy system instead of the Corvus launchers amidships.

In 1987 HMS *Newcastle* became the first Type 42 to be armed with the Phalanx CIWS, these being installed on the platforms abreast the funnel, replacing the twin 30mm mounting. The Phalanx is a self-contained weapon system consisting of a Vulcan 20mm gun with a rate of fire of over 3,000 rounds per minute, target tracking radar and fire control system. It will automatically engage any target which is operating outside preset safety parameters, such as an incoming missile or attacking aircraft. Its engagement range is generally within 1,000m and it is therefore a 'last ditch' defence. All Type 42s should be equipped with this weapon by 1989, considerably enhancing their self-defence capabilities.

A further enhancement is planned for the larger Batch III ships which are programmed to receive a lightweight Seawolf missile system under a contract awarded to British Aerospace early in 1988. This will probably be mounted on the hangar roof, replacing one of the Type 909 tracking radars and will utilise a new four-box launcher instead of the usual 'six-pack' carried on the Type 22 frigates and other ships. It is unlikely that this modification could be made to the short-hulled ships as they lack the necessary stability margins. Nevertheless, all the ships will have a considerably enhanced close range AA armament and should be better able to defend themselves against air attack.

Given the current trends in warship lives, the Type 42s should remain in service until the mid-1990s at least, and the later ships should survive into the 21st century. At the moment, it looks likely that they will be the last warship to bear the title 'destroyer' in the Royal Navy and, despite their inauspicious beginnings, they have become worthy holders of the name.

Above:
HMS *York* on patrol in the Persian Gulf early in 1988. The ship carries two Phalanx CIWS, one of which is visible on the starboard side abreast the funnel — a modification gradually being extended to all Type 42s. Note the single 20mm guns mounted either side of the hangar and the Union Flag draped over the side for additional identification. *HMS York*

Name	No	Laid Down	Launched	Completed	Builder	Yard	Remarks	
Bristol	D23	15/11/67	30/06/69	31/03/73	Swan Hunter	Tyne	Dartmouth Training ship	09/87
Sheffield	D80	15/01/70	10/06/71	28/02/75	Vickers	Barrow	Exocet hit. Sank under tow	10/05/82
Birmingham	D86	28/03/72	30/07/73	03/12/76	Cammell Laird	Birkenhead	In service	1988
Cardiff	D108	06/11/72	22/02/74	19/10/79	Vickers/Swan Hunter	Barrow/Tyne	In service	1988
Coventry	D118	29/01/73	21/06/74	10/11/78	Swan Hunter	Tyne	Sunk air attack, Falklands	25/05/82
Newcastle	D87	21/02/73	24/04/75	23/03/78	Swan Hunter	Tyne	In service	1988
Glasgow	D88	16/04/74	14/04/76	24/05/79	Swan Hunter	Tyne	In service	1988
Exeter	D89	22/07/76	25/04/78	19/09/80	Swan Hunter	Tyne	In service	1988
Southampton	D90	21/10/76	29/01/79	31/10/81	Vosper Thornycroft	Woolston	In service	1988
Nottingham	D91	06/02/78	18/02/80	08/04/83	Vosper Thornycroft	Woolston	In service	1988
Liverpool	D92	05/07/78	25/09/80	09/07/82	Cammell Laird	Birkenhead	In service	1988
Manchester	D95	19/05/78	24/11/80	16/12/82	Vickers SEL	Barrow	In service	1988
Gloucester	D96	29/10/79	02/11/82	11/09/85	Vosper Thornycroft	Woolston	In service	1988
York	D98	18/01/80	21/06/82	09/08/85	Swan Hunter	Tyne	In service	1988
Edinburgh	D97	08/09/80	13/04/83	18/12/85	Cammell Laird	Birkenhead	In service	1988

Data: Batch I Type 42, HMS *Sheffield* (1975)
Displacement (tons): 3,500 standard, 4,100 full load
Length/Beam (ft): 412 (oa)/47
Draught (ft): 19 (full load)
Armament: 1×Mk 8 automatic 4.5in, 2×20mm, GWS 30 Sea Dart SAM system, 1×launcher
Aircraft: Westland Lynx HAS 2 helicopter
Radars: Types 965 (AKE-2), 992Q, 909, 1006
Machinery: COGOG. 2×TM3B Olympus (25,000shp each), 2×RM1A Tyne gas turbines, (4,250shp each), total 58,500shp
Speed/Range: 30kt/4,100nm @ 18kt
Oil Fuel (tons): 600
Complement: 253

Data: Batch III Type 42, HMS *York* (1988)
Displacement (tons): 4,100 standard, 4,775 full load
Length/Beam (ft): 463 (oa)/49
Draught (ft): 19 (full load)
Armament: 1×Mk 8 automatic 4.5in, 4×single 20mm guns, 2×Vulcan/Phalanx CIWS, GWS 30 Sea Dart SAM system, 2×triple ASW TT (STWS-1)
Aircraft: Westland Lynx HAS 3 helicopter
Radars: Types 1022, 992Q, 909(2), 1006
Machinery: As *Sheffield* except for RM1C version of Tyne gas turbine (5,340shp each). Total 54,000shp
Speed/Range: 30kt/4,750nm @ 18kt
Oil Fuel (tons): 610
Complement: 301

For the moment, history of the Navy's destroyers appears to be ending with the Type 42. However, things could have been different. The Navy realised the limitations of a small destroyer built down to a fixed cost and looked ahead to the possibility of building larger ships if the opportunity arose. Considerable work was carried out in the early 1970s on a follow-on design, the Type 43. This would have been powered by four gas turbine engines (possibly the new marine version of the Spey which started development during this period as a result of a RN requirement for a ship to be powered by four 15,000shp units) to make 30kt. Armament would have comprised two independent Sea Dart GWS30 systems, each with two Type 909 radars, two Seawolf GWS25 missile systems, and a Mk 8 4.5in gun. Other weapon systems would have included the STWS-1 with two triple AS torpedo tubes and possibly four Exocet launchers on the stern. The machinery was split into two widely spaced independent units fore and aft, each with its own square-set funnel. Between the funnels was a clear deck space intended for the operation of a Sea King-sized helicopter. From the published artist's impression, there are no obvious hangar facilities although it is possible that one could have been provided below deck with access by lift, although this would have to be situated between the machinery spaces.

There is no doubt that these would have been handsome, powerful and well balanced ships. They would also have been extremely expensive and the projected displacement of around 6,000 tons seems very optimistic. Given the political and financial climate of the times, they were really non-starters and no more than a glimpse at what might have been.

In the immediate future, a requirement for a ship to begin replacing the Type 42s by the mid-1990s has been identified. With Britain's participation in the NATO frigate project (NFR90) currently continuing, these replacements will almost certainly be the air defence variant of this design. Whether these ships will then be referred to as frigates or destroyers remains to be seen. The successful outcome of this part of the NFR90 project depends on the parallel development of a new surface to air missile system to replace Sea Dart. Attempts have already been made to set up a joint programme with the French Navy who have identified a similar requirement but, to date, this has fallen through. Until British participation in the NFR90 programme was confirmed, low-key work on an all-British destroyer design had been started, but it is unlikely that this will ever be built as the pressure to take part in the multi-national programme is too great. With past history in mind, it is likely that the Type 42s will soldier on past their normal life span and any replacement will be late and built in insufficient quantities to maintain the Royal Navy's frontline strength. This book has already shown that most of World War 2 was spent trying to develop ships capable of defending themselves against the contemporary air threat. With that lesson forgotten, the Royal Navy was dispatched to the Falklands with ships plainly unsuitable for the task at hand, and only now are most of its ships armed to the standard shown necessary by the war. We can only hope that the lesson will not need to be learned for a third time!

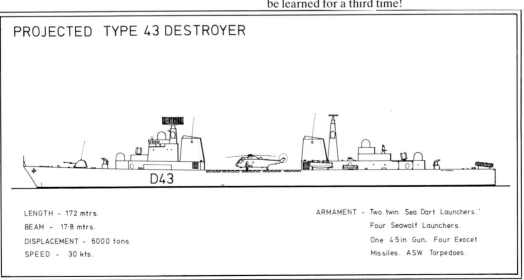

PROJECTED TYPE 43 DESTROYER

D43

LENGTH - 172 mtrs.

BEAM - 17·8 mtrs.

DISPLACEMENT - 6000 tons

SPEED - 30 kts.

ARMAMENT - Two twin Sea Dart Launchers.
Four Seawolf Launchers.
One 4·5in Gun. Four Exocet
Missiles. ASW Torpedoes.

Appendices

1 Disposal List — Prewar Destroyers

At the end of World War 2 the Royal Navy possessed a considerable number of destroyers which had been completed before 1939 and which, for the most part, played no significant role in the postwar period. Most were laid up and subsequently scrapped. Brief details of these survivors and their ultimate fate are given below.

Name	Class	Number	Launched	Disposal
Skate	R (WW1)	H39	1917	Laid up Falmouth 12/44. Scrapped Newport 1947
Sabre	S (WW1)	H18	1918	Scrapped Grangemouth 1946
Saladin	S	H54	1919	Laid up Falmouth 12/44. Scrapped Llanelly 1947
Sardonyx	S	H26	1919	Scrapped Preston 1945
Scimitar	S	H21	1918	Laid up Falmouth 12/44. Scrapped Briton Ferry 1946
Scout	S	H51	1918	Scrapped Briton Ferry 1946
Shikari	S	D85	1919	Scrapped Newport 1945
Thracian	S	D86	1920	Recovered from IJN at Hong Kong 1945. Scrapped 1947
Valourous	V	L00	1917	Scrapped Thornaby 1947
Vanessa	V	I29	1918	Scrapped Charlestown 1949
Vanity	V	L38	1918	Scrapped Grangemouth 1947
Vanoc	V	H33	1917	Wrecked off Penryn while under tow 1946. Scrapped Falmouth
Vanquisher	V	I54	1917	Scrapped Charleston 1948/49
Vega	V	L41	1917	Scrapped Dunston 1948
Velox	V	I34	1917	Scrapped Charlestown 1947
Vendetta	V	I69	1917	RAN 1932. Scuttled off Sydney 1948
Verdun	V	L93	1917	Scrapped Inverkeithing 1946
Versatile	V	I32	1917	Scrapped Granton 1949
Vesper	V	I35	1917	Scrapped Inverkeithing 1948
Vidette	V	I48	1918	Scrapped Grangemouth 1947
Vimy	V	I33	1917	Scrapped Charlestown 1948
Vivacious	V	I36	1917	Scrapped Charlestown 1948
Vivien	V	L33	1918	Scrapped Charlestown 1948
Viceroy	V	L21	1917	Scrapped Grangemouth 1948
Viscount	V	I92	1917	Scrapped Dunston 1947
Walker	W	I27	1917	Scrapped Troon 1946
Watchman	W	I26	1917	Scrapped Inverkeithing 1945
Westcott	W	I47	1918	Scrapped Troon 1946
Westminster	W	L40	1918	Scrapped Rosyth 1948
Winchelsea	W	I46	1917	Scrapped Rosyth 1945
Winchester	W	L55	1918	Accommodation ship 2/45. Scrapped Inverkeithing 1946
Windsor	W	L94	1918	Scrapped Charlestown 1949
Wolfhound	W	I56	1918	Scrapped Granton 1948
Wolsey	W	L02	1918	Scrapped Sunderland 1947
Woolston	W	L49	1918	Scrapped Grangemouth 1947
Vasittart	Mod V	I64	1919	Scrapped Newport 1946
Venomous	Mod V	I75	1918	Scrapped Charlestown 1948
Verity	Mod V	I63	1919	Laid up Barrow 1945. Scrapped Newport 1947
Volunteer	Mod V	I71	1919	Scrapped Granton 1948

Wanderer	Mod W	I74	1919	Scrapped Blyth 1946
Whitehall	Mod W	I94	1919	Scrapped Barrow 1945
Whitshed	Mod W	I77	1919	Scrapped Gateshead 1948
Witherington	Mod W	I76	1919	Wrecked whilst on tow to Charlestown for scrapping 1947
Wivern		I66	1919	Scrapped Charlestown 1948
Wolverine		I78	1919	Scrapped Troon 1946
Worcester	Mod W	I96	1919	Mined 1943. Accommodation ship (*Yeoman*). Scrapped Grays 1947
Wishart	W	I67	1919	Scrapped Inverkeithing 1946
Witch	W	I89	1919	Scrapped Rosyth 1946
Keppel	(Shakespeare)	I84	1920	Scrapped Barrow 1945
Campbell	(Scott)	I60	1918	Scrapped Rosyth 1948
Mackay	(Scott)	I70	1918	Scrapped Charlestown 1949
Malcolm	(Scott)	I19	1919	Scrapped Barrow 1945
Montrose	(Scott)	I01	1918	Scrapped Blyth 1946
Stuart	(Scott)	D00	1918	RAN 1932. Scrapped Sydney 1947
Amazon	(Thornycroft)	I39	1926	Scrapped Troon 1949
Ambuscade	(Yarrow)	I38	1926	Target trials 1947. Scrapped Troon 1947
Active	A	H14	1929	Scrapped Troon 1947
Antelope	A	H36	1929	Scrapped Blyth 1946
Anthony	A	H40	1929	Target trials 1947. Scrapped Troon 1949
Beagle	B	H30	1930	Scrapped Rosyth 1946
Boreas	B	H77	1930	RHN *Salamis* (Greek) 1944-51. Scrapped Troon 1952
Brilliant	B	H84	1930	Damage trials 4/47. Scrapped Troon 1948
Bulldog	B	H91	1930	Scrapped Rosyth 1946
Assiniboine	C	I48	1931	RCN 1939 (ex-*Kempenfelt*). Wrecked Prince Edward Island 1945
Restigouche	C	H00	1931	RCN 1938. (ex-*Comet*). Paid off 1945 and scrapped at Halifax
St Laurent	C	H83	1931	RCN 1937 (ex-*Cygnet*). Paid off 1945 and scrapped at Halifax
Duncan	D (Leader)	I99	1932	Scrapped Barrow 1945
Kootenay	D	H75	1932	RCN 1943 (ex-*Decoy*). Scrapped Halifax 1945
Echo	E	H23	1934	RHN *Navarinon* (Greek) 1944-56. Scrapped Dunston 1956
Escapade	E	H17	1934	Scrapped Grangemouth 1947
Gatineau	E	H61	1934	RCN 1943 (ex-*Express*). Scrapped Victoria 1946
Faulknor	F (Leader)	H62	1934	Scrapped Milford Haven 1946
Fame	F	H78	1934	Dominican *Generalissimo* (1948), *Sanchez* (1962). Laid up 1968
Forester	F	H74	1934	Scrapped Rosyth 1947
Qu'appelle	F	H69	1934	RCN 1944 (ex-*Foxhound*). Scrapped Sydney, Australia, 1946
Garland	G	H37	1935	Polish Navy 1939-47. R.Neth.N. *Marnix* 1947. Scrapped 1964
Ottawa	G	H31	1935	RCN 1943 (ex-*Griffin*). Scrapped Hamilton 1946
Chaudiere	G	H99	1936	RCN 1943 (ex-*Hero*). Scrapped Sydney, Australia, 1950
Hotspur	H	H01	1936	Dominican *Trujillo* 1948, *Duarte* 1962. Laid up 1972
Icarus	I	I03	1936	Scrapped Troon 1946
Ilex	I	I61	1937	Scrapped Italy 1948
Impulsive	I	I11	1937	Scrapped Sunderland 1926
Havelock	(Braz H)	H88	1939	Ex-Brazilian *Jutahy*. Scrapped Inverkeithing 1946
Hesperus	(Braz H)	H57	1939	Ex-Brazilian *Juruena*, ex-*Hearty*. Scrapped Grangemouth 1947
Highlander	(Braz H)	H44	1939	Ex-Brazilian *Jaguaribe*. Scrapped Rosyth 1947
Inconstant	(Turk H)	H49	1941	Ex-Turkish *Mauavenet*. Retroceded 1945. Paid off

During and immediately after the war, destroyers carried pendant numbers consisting of a letter and two numbers for identification and signalling purposes. Fleet destroyers laid down up to around 1942 used flag I and G superior, while later ships used flag R. During 1945 British and Commonwealth destroyers serving in the Pacific used temporary numbers with flag D superior in order to conform with US Navy practice. In most cases this just involved changing the letter, but occasionally the whole group was changed to avoid duplication (eg HMS *Teazer* changed from R23 to D45).

Until 1948, the ships in commission retained their wartime numbers but a new system was then introduced whereby all destroyers were allocated flag D superior. Again a straight change of letter sufficed in most cases, but to avoid duplication some ships had 100 or even 200 added to the original number. Thus HMS *Zest* changed from R02 to D02 while HMS *Whelp* went from R37 to D237 to avoid confusion with HMAS *Tobruk*, a 'Battle' class destroyer laid down in 1946.

The following table lists destroyer pendant numbers with flag D superior issued since 1948. Where appropriate, Commonwealth ships numbers are also included.

Number	Ship	Class
D01	*Caprice*	CA
D02	*Zest*	Z
	Devonshire	County
D03	*Concord*	CO
D04	*Onslaught*	O
	Voyager (RAN)	Daring
D05	*Daring*	Daring
D06	*Myngs*	Z
	Hampshire	County
D07	*Caesar*	CA
D08	*Vendetta*	Daring
D09	*Dunkirk*	Battle
D10	*Cassandra*	CA
D11	*Quadrant* (RAN)	Q
	Vampire (RAN)	Daring
D12	*Kent*	County
D14	*Armada*	Battle
D15	*Cavendish*	CA
D16	*London*	County
D17	*Alamein*	Battle
D18	*St Kitts*	Battle
	Antrim	County
D19	*Zephyr*	Z
	Glamorgan	County
D20	*Comus*	CO
	Fife	County
D21	*Chivalrous*	CH
	Norfolk	County
D22	*Aisne*	Battle
D23	*Teazer*	T
	Bristol	Type 82
D24	*Gravelines*	Battle
D25	*Carysfort*	CA
D26	*Comet*	CO
D27	*Savage*	S
D28	*Verulam*	V
D29	*Charity*	CH
D30	*Carron*	CA
D31	*Broadsword*	Weapon
D32	*Camperdown*	Battle
D33	*Terpsichore*	T
D34	*Cockade*	CO
D35	*Diamond*	Daring
D36	*Chieftain*	CH
D37	*Tobruk* (RAN)	Battle
D38	*Nizam*	N
D39	*Zealous*	Z
D40	*Troubridge*	T
D41	*Volage*	V
D43	*Matapan*	Battle
D44	*Lagos*	Battle
D45	*Tenacious*	T

Below:
One destroyer not mentioned in the text is HMS *Nonsuch*. Originally the German destroyer Z38 shown here, she was briefly commissioned into the Royal Navy after the war for trials with her high pressure machinery, before being used as a test target for underwater explosions. She was scrapped in 1950. *Real Photos (1935)*

No	Name	Class	No	Name	Class
D047	Gabbard	Battle	D106	Decoy	Daring
D048	Contest	CO	D108	Dainty	Daring
D049	Onslow	O		Cardiff	Type 42
D050	Venus	V	D114	Defender	Daring
D051	Chevron	CH	D115	Raider	R Class
D052	Chaplet	CH	D118	Battleaxe	Weapon
D053	Undaunted	U		Coventry	Type 42
D054	Zodiac	Z	D119	Delight	Daring
D055	Finisterre	Battle	D121	Tumult	T
D056	Petard	P	D123	Warramunga (RAN)	Tribal
D057	Cossack	CO	D125	Nepal	N
D058	Milne	M	D126	Diana	Daring
D059	Anzac (RAN)	Battle	D129	Offa	O
D060	Sluys	Battle	D130	Arunta (RAN)	Tribal
D061	Chequers	CH	D135	Marne	M
D062	Jutland	Battle	D138	Rapid	R
D064	Scorpion	Weapon	D139	Obdurate	O
D065	St James	Battle	D141	Redoubt	R
D066	Zambesi	Z	D142	Undine	U
D067	Tyrian	T	D149	Norman	N
D068	Barrosa	Battle	D154	Duchess	Daring
D069	Paladin	P	D156	Tuscan	T
D070	Solebay	Battle	D158	Wrangler	W
D071	Constance	CO	D159	Wakeful	W
D072	Wizard	W	D168	Crispin	CR
D073	Cavalier	CA	D169	Ulysses	U
D074	Hogue	Battle	D180	Opportune	O
D075	Virago	V	D186	Musketeer	M
D076	Consort	CO	D187	Whirlwind	W
D077	Trafalgar	Battle	D189	Termagent	T
D078	Wessex	W	D191	Bataan (RAN)	Tribal
D079	Cadiz	Battle	D195	Roebuck	R
D080	Barfleur	Battle	D197	Grenville	U
	Sheffield	Type 42	D198	Orwell	O
D081	Zebra	Z	D199	Urchin	U
D082	Creole	CR	D209	Rotherham	R
D083	Ulster	U	DDE213	Nookta (RCN)	Tribal
D084	Saintes	Battle	DDE214	Micmac (RCN)	Tribal
D085	Cambrian	CA	DDE215	Haida (RCN)	Tribal
D086	Agincourt	Battle	DDE216	Huron (RCN)	Tribal
	Birmingham	Type 42	DDE217	Iroquois (RCN)	Tribal
D87	Newcastle	Type 42	DDE218	Cayuga (RCN)	Tribal
D88	Glasgow	Type 42	DDE219	Athabaskan (RCN)	Tribal
D89	Exeter	Type 42	D222	Ursa	U
D90	Cheviot	CH	DDE224	Valentine (RCN)	V
	Southampton	Type 42	DDE225	Vixen (RCN)	V
D91	Childers	CH	DDE226	Crescent (RCN)	CR
	Nottingham	Type 42	DDE228	Crusader (RCN)	CR
D92	Liverpool	Type 42	D231	Vigo	Battle
D93	Vigilant	V	D237	Whelp	W
D95	Zenith	Z	D248	Obedient	O
	Manchester	Type 42	D252	Matchless	M
D96	Crossbow	Weapon	D262	Quality (RAN)	Q
	Gloucester	Type 42	D270	Queenborough (RAN)	Q
D97	Corruna	Battle	D273	Meteor	M
	Edinburgh	Type 42	D281	Quiberon (RAN)	Q
D98	York	Type 42	D292	Quickmatch (RAN)	Q
D103	Kempenfelt	W	D297	Napier	N
D105	Urania	U	D298	Wager	W

Bibliography

The following publications contain much of the background information necessary for a book such as this. The author gratefully acknowledges the work and research already carried out by the writers of the books listed here.

British Destroyers 1892-1953; Edgar J. March; Seeley Service and Co, 1966.

Combat Fleets of the World (various editions); Jean Labayle Couhat (Ed); Arms and Armour Press.

Janes Fighting Ships (various editions); Janes Yearbooks.

Warships of the British and Commonwealth Navies; H. T. Lenton; Ian Allan Ltd, 1966 and 1969.

British Fleet and Escort Destroyers (two vol); H. T. Lenton; MacDonald and Co (Publishers) Ltd, 1970.

British Warships; H. T. Lenton; Ian Allan Ltd, 1958 and 1962.

British Warships Since 1945 (Part 3) Destroyers; Mike Critchley; Maritime Books, 1982.

Destroyer Weapons of World War 2; Peter Hodges/Norman Friedman; Conway Maritime Press, 1979.

A Century of Naval Construction; D. K. Brown, RCNC; Conway Maritime Press, 1983.

All the World's Fighting Ships 1947-1982, Part I; Conway Maritime Press, 1983.

The Metal Fighting Ship in the Royal Navy 1860-1970; E. H. H. Archibald; Blandford Press, 1971.

Fighting Ships of the World; Antony Preston (Ed); Hamlyn Publishing Group Ltd, 1980.

The Postwar Naval Revolution; Norman Friedman; Conway Maritime Press, 1986.

Naval Weapons of World War Two; John Campbell; Conway Maritime Press, 1985.

Tribal Class Destroyers; Peter Hodges; Almark Publications, 1971.

Battle Class Destroyers; Peter Hodges; Almark Publications, 1971.

HMS Cavalier, Profile No 32; Antony Preston; Profile Publications Ltd, 1973.

Warship (quarterly periodical — various editions); Conway Maritime Press, 1977-1988.

Ships Monthly (periodical — various editions); Waterway Publications Ltd.

Below:
HMS *Echo* was transferred to the Greek Navy in 1944 and renamed *Navarinon*. She is shown here in 1953 at the Spithead Coronation Review but was scrapped three years later. *Maritime Photo Library*